B
Joh
Levi, V.   NA-804
From a Far Country
Story of Karol Wojtyla

FROM A FAR COUNTRY

The Story of Karol Wojtyła in Poland

by

A. Kijowski e J.J. Szczepański

with the collaboration of K. Zanussi

written by V. Levi

ERI / NEFF

FROM A FAR COUNTRY

PRESENTATION

This is a true story: a story of a man who was born and lived in Poland between 1920 and 1978. He is successively a student, a worker, an actor, a poet: then a priest teaching in a university, a bishop, a cardinal. One day he was made a Pope. From then on he lived in Rome—truly a universal man, but with Poland in his heart. It is the story of Karol Wojtyła.

There is another true story: that of a suffering and bold people, who passed through terrible trials during those very same years, struggling because, after enduring the trials, they could affirm those things in which they believed. It is the story of Poland during the last ten years.

And then, it is also an invented story, that of Władek and Staszek, of Tadeusz and of Wanda, of Marian, of Józef, of Magda, which, grafted in the first two, gives color to the grand fresco of the film—the film which Krzysztof Zanussi conceived and produced with superb art, and together with Andrzej Kijowski and Jan Szczepanski dramatized with historical accuracy and warm fantasy.

The book which I am presenting is a faithful and rapid transposition, in story form, of the film and its characters. It is a story of our times, true in great part, similar in others: it is a beautiful story which shows and gives courage, and in which the light of the persons prevails over the darkness of many global happenings.

This work is meant to prepare, to accompany, and to complete the viewing of the film and also to bring a deeper understanding to those who wish to go beyond the mere pictures.

ALBERTO LUNA
The Publisher

Good Friday, 1926

"Wake up, Lolek. It's time!"

The child makes a face, shakes his head, rubs his eyes with tight fists and is on his feet with a jump, standing next to the bed. He has been waiting for this day for some time. Papa Karol has promised him that this time he will take him along to Kalwaria, down there on the hill among the trees, with the people who are coming from Cracow, and down from Nowy Targ and from Zakopane, who flock from Katowice and from Chestochowa and of course from Wadowice, the town where the Wojtylas live.

"The snow is still high in Kalwaria. Cover up well. Wear your boots and lace them tight. Don't forget your fur hat."

Lolek doesn't have to be told twice. He is ready in a moment and standing next to his father, who finishes loading the knapsack with food for the day.

Outside it is still dark. In the great Polish sky the stars shine. The bracing air stings the child's face. But there is warm pride in the boy's heart, the pride of being grown, of being six years old, of being allowed to go with his father toward an adventure he has long dreamed of in the mysterious Kalwaria woods.

There, many years ago — nearly three hundred years ago — a lord of Cracow, leader of the vaivode, had built a church to the Madonna and had

9

surrounded it with chapels more than forty of them, each dedicated to one of the mysteries in the lives of Christ and Mary. The chapels are scattered in the birch-and-beech wood. Small pats (*drozki*), connect them. Starting from the church, they cover the stages of the redemption from God's promise of early Paradise to the Annunciation, to the Nativity, to the Passion, to the Crucifixion, up to the Resurrection. But the high point is the Calvary. And since the name of the lord was Mikolaj Zebrzydowski, the sanctuary is named Kalwaria Zebrzydowska.

During the year many pilgrims came to the Madonna's beautiful church, especially in the good season. The feast of the Assumption in mid-August saw peasants bringing sheaves of wheat and rye and the fruits of the countryside, along with flags, crosses and rosaries on which they prayed, to be blessed. But at Easter a pilgrimage was essential, for a Passion Play was presented in Kalwaria. And no matter how often the weather was still wintery, no matter how much snow, packed or melting, was still on the ground, many people came, leaving at daybreak or even before from the villages and surrounding cities, traveling the long or short distance on foot and using farm wagons only when necessary.

Karol, a middle-aged man with an austere face that relects his military training (he has been a junior officer in the army commissary) has a soft spot for his little boy, his second-born who has come after many years. He wants him with him as soon as possible, to share life's most beautiful experiences. He has a clear premonition of how the child's intelligence and sensitivity might develop.

In no time they leave the village behind them and join the streams of pilgrims flowing toward the pats that lead to Kalwaria, and in the pauses between the prayers and songs they talk to each other.''

''Daddy, my shoe hurts.''

The father kneels and fixes the boy's shoe, and speaks to him of Jesus, whom Lolek himself will soon see with his own eyes, bent beneath the cross, walking toward Calvary.

A few hours later, in a straw-thatched peasants' hut a few feet from the sanctuary, a rite is being executed that takes in all generations. The father, Zapala, a vigorous peasant about fifty years old, is the one who will play the role of the suffering Christ in the sacred play, as his father has done and as his son Wladek, now a boy no more than ten, will one day do. For the occasion Zapala has let his hair and beard grow; he has prepared his soul with annual confession. But he also has to purify his body. In the center of

10

the room is a tub filled with steaming water that will be used for his bath shortly before the beginning of the rite. His wife and oldest daughter will assist him, rubbing his back and shoulders and drying him. Then the man will dress in the white robe that lies on a table near his daughter, and will don a bramble wreath to represent the crown of thorns. The women hurry the father so he won't be late. In front of the house the neighbors have brought the great wooden cross that Zapala will hoist on his shoulders. Even little Wladek helps them carry it. His father watches, pleased.

It is time. On Kalwaria Hill the wind raises windmills of snow. But the people stand silent, heedless of the cold as they await the sacred spectacle that will touch their hearts.

Then it is noon, Pilate's hour. Roman legionaires with their helmets and shields of cardboard and tin advance toward the Governor's podium. It is the terrace of the Francescan convent annexed to the sanctuary. From on high Pilate is easily visible to the crowd that has gathered; his despicable gestures are received in silence: a legionaire pours water from a pitcher onto his hands; the words, "I am innocent of the blood of this just man" are heard. The route of the cross begins. The heavy wood hangs on the shoulders of the father Zapala, who has become for all present Jesus. The Redeemer advances barefooted in the snow, dragging the weight, prodded by soldiers on both sides. A group of women moan for him. One of them makes her way through the soldiers; it is Zapala's daughter Veronica. In her hand she holds a cloth of white linen with which she moves to clean the sweat and blood that run down Christ's face. When she turns, all see, impressed on the linen, the image of the suffering Savior.

"Daddy, how did they do that?" little Lolek asks his father, who is holding his hand. But instead of answering, his father motions him to be silent. It is not the time for explanations, it is a time for impressions that must enter the child's heart and stay there forever, while the adults contemplate and reflect. Shortly afterward, Christ falls, crushed by the weight of the wood. The crowd kneels, moved. Soldiers beat the fallen man with whips; he rises arduously, shoulders the cross once more, and continues hi walk. Finally the cross is erected on Calvary Hill and stands perpendicular to the kneeling crowd. Lolek hasn't missed a moment of the play. Now awed, now with his eyes wide open in wonder, now silent, now asking his father a question, he has seen everything. But his curiosity is still not satisfied. Pushing through the crowd, he is soon out of his father's sight. Where has he gone?

By now it is growing dark and among the trees fires are being lit; people warm themselves and are having something to eat, in an atmosphere that little by little changes from somber and still to festive and gay in the spirit of Easter. But Wojtyla is disturbed. Lolek is nowhere to be seen and does not answer his father's calls. The man approaches a shivering policeman on duty near the sanctuary.

"You haven't seen a little boy about so tall with a fur cap on his head?" The agent does no more than make note of the name in his notebook. The father, still searching, enters a tavern which is filled with hot and thirsty people. Even the legionaires are sitting around at the tables still wearing their shiny armaments. The Christ, too, is among them with a stein of beer in his hand. In a corner all alone, his eyes wide open, is little Lolek, observing the scene.

"Lolek, what are you doing here?" his father exclaims.

"Daddy," he stammers, "he's drinking beer."

"He's drinking because he's tired," his father says. "Come. It's time to be on our way home."

But Lolek is not convinced. There is something he does not understand.

"Come now," his father says. "This isn't the truth, it's only theater...."

12

KAROL WOJTYLA JUNIOR

Little Lolek from Kalwaria, Karol Wojtyla Junior, was born on May 18, 1920 in Wadowice, a town of fifteen thousand people located some twenty or thirty kilometers southeast of Cracow, on which the town depends. His family was much like other peasant families. His father was a junior career officer, his older broter a doctor. Karol's mother died when the boy was nine years old. Later, in 1929, his older brother died of a sudden illness. He lived alone with his lather until the beginning of 1941, when his father died. From his family he inherited, along with an uncommonly healthy physique and makeup (including his basic temperament), a humane and Christian upbringing which gave the child, the teenager and the young man Karol a special equilibrium.

He attended elementary and secondary schools in Wadowice. During his last year at the lyceé, his school was honored by a visit by Prince Adam Stefan Sapieha, Archbishop of Cracow. Karol was chosen to welcome him. It is said that the Archbishop was so favorably impressed by the young man's personality that he asked him if he would consider entering the priesthood. Woityla said no. He was thinking of studying Polish literature, and that is what he did, enrolling in 1938 in Jagellonica University in Cracow.

During his years in Wadowice, he had shown his sociable nature, joining

13

in his friends' games, participating in sports and, with special preference, working in theater. When he came to Cracow, where there was much interest in theater, he took part as an actor in a recently constituted theater, trying his hand at poetry as well with friends who shared his creative bent. After the death of his father, these friends became his new family.

It was the eve of World War II. While Karol Wojtyla was enrolling for his second year of Polish literature at Cracow University, Germans and Russians invaded Poland. It was the fourth time the country had been divided. Previous partitionings were in 1772, 1793 and, most gravely, 1815. This time Poland was absorbed to the east and to the west by the two powers. By Hitler's order, in the center from the Tatra Mountains to Pomerania, a governorship was created on October 12, 1939, and placed under the direct dependency of the cruel governor General Hans Frank, whose headquarters were in the historic Wawel Castle in Cracow.

THE GERMANS IN CRACOW

Near the castle is the cathedral. In the most sacred city in Poland, sacred for its history and its art and culture, there is a hill, Wawel Hill. On its steep summit, high over the Vistola Valley, the spires of the cathedral stand out against the sky. Three times the sanctuary has been rebuilt in the course of the centuries. Here is Poland's treasure and its heart. The history of the country's art is stratified, built into the cathedral walls and into the monuments found on its holy perimeters. The altar of Stanislao the Martyr, built on the crypt of Saint Leonard, in memory Saint Wenceslaus, and on the remains of Saint Florian, is surrounded by the tombs of kings, bishops and saints. In the many lateral chapels live the vestiges of a glorious history. It is here that for centuries the nation's sovereigns were crowned; here that the gigantic Sigismondd bell tolls the country's most important hours. To this hill, sanctuary and eloquent monument to the nation's grandeur, the hearts of all Poles turn in prayer for the spiritual and moral continuity of the generations.

It is here, on an autumn evening in 1939, that a patrol of German soldiers, cocky with the easy success of their treacherous invasion, come. Having surrounded the rock — having observed its majesty from the Straszewski Road and from the byways of the Planty Gardens through the thick boughs of the trees, they take the Kanonicza Road, their cars climbing

15

the steep hill that leads to the courtyard in front of the cathedral. They climb out there, banging doors and stomping heavily on the sacred soil. They demand that the old vicar of the church open the building for them.

The group hurries toward the steps that lead to the main doors. The thin, bent priest puffs his way up the steps, clutching a bunch of keys in his perspiring hands; the Germans follow behind him. Shut tight and shaded as it is, the black stone door with its wooden knockers covered in bronze (on which is stamped the letter K, the initial of King Kasimir the Great, the founder) seems determined to resist the imminent profanation. For a moment the invaders seem embarrassed. But the officer in charge breaks the silence.

"Won't these fall?" he asks the priest as he studies the great fossil bones which date from the ice age and which hang from chains to the left of the doorways above the gothic sculptures that decorate the sides of the door. These are the oldest vestiges of animal life, an object of wonder for the people in olden days, and for this reason they have been kept near the church.

"When they fall it will mean the end of the world," the priest answers with knowing calm.

"Is that a legend?" asks another.

And the priest, with a slow gesture of his hand, says only, "We'll see...."

Then he inserts a huge key into the keyhole of the small door located in the lower part of the right-hand door, turns it, opens the small entrance with a sigh, and stepping aside with meek resignation, makes way for the soldiers.

With a clanging of boots and metal, the men wearing red armbands decorated with black swastikas, the men with their caps bearing emblems of skulls and eagles holding the profaned cross, burst into the sacred hall, taking brutal possession of it. The priest kneels and removes his hat; the others, hats on their heads, roam through the nave, observe, comment. They like the acoustics; the cathedral shall become a concert hall. And what is that arc full of ornaments doing there in the center of the hall? Is it the tomb of Saint Stanislao, martyr to the faith and patron saint of Poland? Good. It will be removed. In fast, it ruins the perspective! Why keep the toms of King Ladislao Jagellone, King Ladislao Warnenczyk, Cardinal Frederick Jagellone, son of Kasimir? And those of Queen Edwig and King Ladislao the Brief? And the chapels? What a waste of richness, they weaken the acoustics in the central area!

They take the inside stairs and head for the crypts. Here are the graves of the poets Adam Mickiewicz and Juliusz Slowacki, of the national heroes Jan

16

Sobieski, Josef Poniatowski and Tadeusz Kosciuzko, of many kings and queens of Poland. They glance at the names. They pat the Roman columns.

"The emigrants, the poets, the suicides, the bumbling kings, the legends, the miracles..." The officer speaks emphatically, full of himself. "All this is literature, not the life of a state. That is why we are here. And we will not leave. At last there will be a State. A German State."

"*Fortuna variabilis, Deus mirabilis,*" the old priest murmurs. "They are the very words that one of my predecessors uttered nearly three hundred years ago to the King of Sweden, who told him the very things you are telling me today. And he said them in the same circumstances."

The German shakes his head, exploding, "History! Always history! They are your dreams... Well, go ahead and sleep, sleep peacefully. You're of no use to anyone."

They are back at the entrance, but the Germans linger still. The old priest hazards submissively, "I would like to close the church."

The German reaches out and snatches the keys from the old man. "There's no need. I'll keep these keys."

The Terror Begins

Nearly fourteen years have passed since the day Lolek Wojtyla saw
Zapala carry the cross. The man and his wife have grown old, but their son
Wladek is a strong young man married to a young woman who has given him
a son. The house is the same as before; life goes on there between work in the
fields and forests, devotions at the sanctuary, and the Passion Play on Good
Friday each year.

It is a quiet autumn afternoon. The women are at home doing housework.
The mother, seated on a low stool near a lukewarm stove, is peeling potatoes.
Her daughter-in-law sits on a wooden bench feeding porridge from a spoon
to a child of about two. The men are in the barn quartering and cleaning a
huge pig that is strung from a rafter. It is against the laws of the invaders,
but who is ever going to come as far as Kalwaria looking for illegal meat?

The two women are startled when the door of the house flies open and a
neighbor rushes in.

''Is your husband home?'' she demands.

''He's working in the barn with Wladek.''

''The Nazis are in the village, they're searching everywhere for meat.''

The young woman jumps to her feet and sets down the child, who has begun to scream. She begins to head for the barn, but her neighbor, watching out the window, exclaims in despair, "My God, they're coming!"

Two armed men, one in civilian clothes and another in uniform, arrive at the doorway while a truck full of guards makes its way behind the yard.

"Wladek, run!" shouts the young woman.

But the two Germans are already headed for the barn and after the woman's cry they begin to run. With a yank, Wladek pulls a plank from the wall, runs out and flees, but the old man doesn't make it in time. The two Germans take him, drag him to the truck, load him on and then turn to the women who have rushed, shouting and crying, to defend the man. Other peasants from the area have been captured and loaded onto the army truck. The curtain is lowered and the vehicle departs, followed by the women's laments, the barking of the dogs and the cries of the children.

Wladek has run into the bushes along the steep slopes that lead to a little river that laps against the hillside. A soldier has spotted him and has shouldered his rifle, taken aim, and fired. Wladek feels the atrocious caress of the bullet against his cheek, but he doesn't surrender. He keeps rolling downhill till he hits the water under the little footbridge. There he hides, pressing his wounded cheek with a cloth, and waits like a hunted animal for events to unfold. Sometime later a heavy army truck shakes the boards of the bridge and then rumbles off into the distance.

Many months have passed. It is August 14, 1941, and in the immense camp at Oswiecim, which the Germans call Auschwitz, the deportees live between life and death, between debilitating slave labor and the gas chamber. Oswiecimm is only a few kilometers from Kalwaria, but for the prisoner Zapala it is as though he were in another hemisphere. There is no contact with the outside world, food is poor and scarce. There is cruelty, exhaustion, a terrible winter and a torrid summer — no comfort. His strength ebbs despite the solidarity of his fellow inmates and the internal resistance.

This morning the prisoners are lined up in the camp's main yard and left standing for hours and hours. Before the ranks of men in stripes, the lords of the camp stroll cynically. They are Lagerfürer Fritsch, his second Palitsch, and SS men with their dogs on leashes. The silence is ghostly, broken only by the crunching of gravel under the leaders' boots and now and then by the sound of Fritsch's whip cracking against his boot. From time to time, he checks his watch.

Old Zapala can no longer stand. Before his delirious eyes, Fritsch is transformed into a Roman centurion, his comrades into legionaires, and he, the Christ of Kalwaria, falls beneath the cross while some whip him and others try to raise him to his feet. He seems to hear the plaintive chant of the crowd; this time it is finished. Exhausted, he remains on the ground among his comrades forced into immobility.

It is now that Fritsch decides. He murmurs something to Palitsch. The Germans stop and Palitsch, in broken Polish, speaks to the prisoners. One of their comrades has fled, but the SS will find him. In the meantime, as a lesson, ten prisoners will be chosen at random and will be left to die of hunger in a bunker.

A chill spreads among the human larva still on its feet. Fritsch begins slowly walking past the columns. Now and then he taps a man with his whip; those tapped step forward and Palitsch writes down their serial numbers. Then an SS man with a dog leads these men aside. The drama takes place in absolute silence until one of the men chosen breaks into a horrendous cry of pain and rebellion. He doesn't want to die, he can't die; his children, his wife, can't live without him. With a kick a guard pushes him brutally toward the condemned men.

In that moment, from the column of motionless prisoners comes a little man with glasses. He holds his cap against his striped pantleg and draws himself to attention before Fritsch. Palitsch rushes toward the man, to teach him a lesson. But Fritsch stops him.

"What is it?" he asks.

"Herr Lagerfürer, allow me to take this man's place."

More curious than amazed, Fritsch asks him, "Who are you?"

"I am a Catholic priest. My name is Raymond Kolbe. I am called Maximilian."

Fritsch and the other Germans stare at him silently for a while. Among the prisoners, tension mounts. Anything can happen, probably a scene of inhuman violence. But Fritsch, with a sardonic tone, finds in this novelty an unexpected form of sadism, and nodding his head says, "Fine!"

Palitsch takes Kolbe's number and sends him toward the condemned group. The prisoner who has been saved is in tears, still undone, and returns to take his place in the column.

The selection is done. An SS man gives the order:

"Right face!" The group, surrounded by agents with dogs, leaves the yard headed for the death bunker.

Palitsch orders the ranks back to their barracks. There is a moment of confusion, the barking dogs give the scene a cruel flavor. Everyone goes, but there are corpses on the ground, among them old Zapala. The camp leader and his henchmen order the prisoners to remove the bodies. Several of them approach the dead and lift the bodies by arms and legs. They drag them across the dusty yard and pile them up at the base of one of the barracks walls.

The Torment and Resources of the Youngs

The Nazi steamroller was leveling Europe. In the Germans' plan there was no room for a Polish nation, a Polish state. The Polish people were to serve only as a labor force. Consequently Polish culture was condemned to annihilation: schools were closed, as were universities, museums, libraries, theaters, the most beautiful churches. Young men were rounded up in the streets and houses to be sent to Germany for forced labor. Several escaped deportation — those assigned to work in the factories and on local services. These men were judged necessary for the war economy. For this reason many university students went from the schools to manual labor. Studies continued in secret, after work. And so did artistic activity, especially theater.

In theater the Poles found expression for their patriotic sentiments and strength to counter within their spirit the dark night, perhaps the most terrible night, that had once again fallen over the nation's destiny. The lessons and recitals held in private homes constituted a violation of the law. Violators risked severe sanctions.

Young Wojtyla became a worker as well, first a miner and then a laborer in the Solvay chemical plant in Cracow. Thus he was able to avoid persecution and at the same time continue, in secret, his university studies and his theatrical activity. He joined the theater of Mieczyslaw Kotlarczyk, a man whose students called him "professor" and in whose private home they gathered nearly every day to try and stage the nation's classics.

It is dawn, an autumn dawn laced with fog and vapor that falls heavier than elsewere on the Solvay plant, where smokestacks pour smoke and gaseous residue out over the city. The factory is located on the southern outskirts of Cracow, on a flat road that becomes, little by little, a winding, steep incline. Truck and machine traffic is heavy; engines rumble, horns blare, and the tracks of white headlights and red taillights, although dimmed according to blackout regulations, create strange arabesques in the liquid morning mists. Everything is covered with a whitish color created by the dust of sodium minerals that blankets the roads and factory installations. In the distance, as though rising from invisible waters, are the spires of Wawel. The night shift is almost over, the sirens sound, the gates open, the workers come forward one by one, hands raised to be frisked before leaving the premises. Then they set out, wary, along the narrow sidewalk that marks the pedestrian lane dividing the main street, which is used by traffic, from an unprotected line of tracks used by freight cars moving the factory's material.

There is a sudden thudding sound. Something has fallen onto the street, either thrown from a truck or felled by one. The light is still too weak to see what has happened. An old woman who is walking toward the city approaches, stops, bends over. A man has fallen to the ground and lies inert as a mannequin. From his forehead a large spot of blood is spreading over the ground. He is lying in an extremely precarious position there by the roadside; any passing vehicle could run over him, crush him.

The woman rises, shouts, waves her arms trying to stop someone. But the cars pass by. One does stop and a soldier climbs out, swearing at the woman — he was almost forced to run over her. But when he sees the body on the ground, the body of a young man bleeding badly, he signals the other soldiers to climb down, too.

They stand silently before him. They have seen deaths and wounds of all kinds, but when it is a young man something must be done. A soldier murmurs, "We have to remove him." The officer, almost relieved at not having to take the initiative in an act of kindness, orders, "All right, get him out of here!"

They load him onto the car and drive off while the old woman stands crying at the scene of the accident.

From the opposite direction the workers from the morning shift are returning. They approach the scene and are curious. They surround the

24

woman; one casts the light of his flashlight on the puddle where the body lay and sees the blood. Nearby he sees a briefcase, all muddied. He picks it up, tries to wipe it with his sleeve, and then exclaims, "This is Lolek's!"

On the afternoon of the following day, the "professor" is rehearsing in his home with his students. Chairs and armchairs are pushed off to one side around a table and sofa — they represent the audience. The rest of the room is the stage. The first job is to place the actors. The "professor" is careful and guides and coaches them as though he were placing sculptures in an art show.

It is daylight, but the room is poorly lit. Handmade lace curtains hang at the windows. On the walls are paintings darkened with age and framed in heavy gilt. The pendulum clock tick-tocks and there are muffled sounds of wood splintering and crackling in the over of the high majolica stove. One of the actors, a long skinny fellow, is bothered by the opaque glass lamp that hangs low into the center of the room.

"Wanda, get closer to the window; turn around so we can see Mietek...." The professor is giving instructions to a girl with thick, copper-colored hair, a slender figure, and a serious, distinct face. Mietek is the skinny fellow near the lamp, the one with a sad clown face that makes no one laugh. The professor's eyes are feverish. Concentration is painted on his thin-lipped face. Each time he opens his mouth it is as though he were pronouncing an oracle, a new truth, a discovery.

"Mietek, look there, not toward her! Your gazes run parallel, they never meet. We are together but each is a world unto himself..."

Wanda watches him with enthusiasm and devotion. She drinks in his every word and scrupulously follows his direction. Mietek, on the other hand, doesn't appreciate such scrupulousness and watches the professor with a touch of irony.

The professor, who is wearing a sporty but threadbare suit with knee-britches and a bow-tie, stops, stares at a spot on the floor, thinks a moment and says, "Karol will stand here. For now I will take his part. His confession is the main theme of the scene. Listen to it and concentrate on it, really feel it as though each of you were saying it yourself, as though you were listening to your own sins..."

"Can't we wait a little longer until Karol gets here?" Wanda ventures timidly.

"No!" answers the professor firmly. "When he comes..."

Just then the doorbell rings. "There he is!" Wanda squeals and runs into the hall. But unlike their signal, the bell has rung only once. Immediately Mietek realizes what this means.

"It's an outsider."

"Quickly, everyone, the snack —. Everyone group around the table!" The scene is rapidly transformed. A tablecloth is spread, copies of the script hidden underneath it. Snacks that each has brought are laid out on the table and everyone sits down, assuming a relaxed, casual attitude, but inside they tremble and expect the worst.

Wanda opens the door and sees before her two young men in blue work overalls with gray caps and metal badges. One is her brother Marian, the other a stranger.

Wanda, who in the few moments from the living room to the door had realized the danger and had opened with her heart in her throat, breathes a sigh of relief.

"Is that you, Marian?"

"Yes, and this is Tadek. We work together. We're bringing bricks to the governor's palace."

The two are part of the Baudienst, the building service which keeps them from being deported to Germany. Marian has Tadeusz with him. He wants to introduce him to the group as an aspiring actor. Their excuse is that they have come to watch the show. "But there is no show today," Wanda says quietly. Marian is disappointed. "And today we were able to get leave... I promised Tadeusz I'd bring him." Then he whispers, "You know, he'd like to act..."

At the end of the corridor the door opens brusquely and the professor appears.

"Who is it?"

"This is my brother Marian and this is his friend," Wanda says. "They came to see the show."

"But there is no show today. We've postponed it."

Then Wanda reveals the young visitors' intentions, telling the professor that Tadeusz would like to act. Marian praises his friend: "He's very talented, he used to act in school."

The professor studies Tadeusz attentively. The young man submits to the scrutiny with embarrassment, biting his lip and lowering his eyes.

"We don't act," the professor declares, "we meditate." Then after a pause, "What do you know?"

"A little of everything," Tadek answers. "A lot of Mickiewicz."

The professor admits the young men and they go inside to the group,

26

which is enjoying itself. Several are munching biscuits. Mietek is dancing with a girl who is laughing gaily.

"There's nothing wrong," the professor says. "Let's get back to work. This is Tadek, he'll stand in for Karol."

Quickly the young people put things away, take out their scripts again from under the tablecloth, and resume their places while Mietek the improvisor wolfs down a last cake.

The professor tells Tadek, "We're preparing several excerpts from the poem *Pan Tadeusz* by Mickiewicz. Our method is to speak the parts. Each tells them in his own way, expressing to himself the characters or scene he has chosen; each on his own from his place. The placing is most important. You have to stand in for someone who is not here today. Now you are he. Take the text and read it as best you can."

Tadek is happy. He knows Jacek Soplita's confession. He recited it in his high school before the war. Marian says he did it well, but the professor pays no attention to Marian. He silences him with a gesture of comic horror.

Wanda sits down on the floor next to Marian. Her brother asks her what has happened, why is the professor so tense? She says that Karol kasn't shown up and isn't home either. Taked asks, "Did they get him?"

Wanda shrugs. But she is worried and afraid. Meanwhile someone sits down at the piano and plays a chord. When the notes have faded and silence has returned, the professor gives Tadeusz the signal to begin.

Tadeusz, after a moment of concentration begins speaking in an uncertain voice. But suddenly he is interrupted by the voice of a radio announcer. It says in Gemran, "The Wehrmacht High Command announces, fromt he Fuhrer's head-quarters..."

Tadeusz stops with a disappointed motion. Everyone watches him to see what he will do next. Aware that he is the center of attention, Tadeusz raises his voice and almost yells to drown out the voice on the loudspeaker. But suddenly the announcer is silent; perhaps there is a mechanical failure, perhaps he has simply stopped. Tadek's shout lingers in the air with unpleasant dissonance.

There is a short, silent pause. Then Tadeusz asks if he should start again. But the professor says no, it is better to stop, everyone is too nervous. Wanda says firmly:

"I'm going to Tyniecka Street."

"Go! But not alone," says the professor.

Marian offers to go with her. "They won't stop the Baudienst!"

Tadeusz jumps at the double opportunity, the first of getting out of the professor's scrutiny (given his unfavorable debout), and the second of going with Wanda, whom he likes a lot. He says impulsively, "Did I do poorly, or don't you need me?"

The answer is not unkind. "Come another time. We'll see. Anyway, the same thing happened to Karol a few days ago. They turned on the loudspeaker while he was reciting. I thought an actor should stop and wait."

Upset at the memory, the professor leaves the room and Mietek takes up his story for him with a slightly teasing tone. Their "leader" had said, in fact, that in similar circumstances it was best to stand absolutely still as a stone, retreat into one's self, and let the evil voice go in one ear and out the other. Then when it stopped, begin again where one had left off.

But what had Karol done? He had gone ahead without raising his voice by even half a note. They couldn't hear him at all, but they understood every word. They seemed to hear the words because they saw them... And moving his hand with a complicated gesture, Mietek shows how to hear by sight alone.

When Wanda, Marian and Tadek get to Tyniecka Street they find some tenants huddled in the entranceway around an old workman dressed in sodium-stained overalls. In his hand is a briefcase spotted with mud and blood.

"That's Karol's briefcase!" Wanda exclaims apprehensively.

The workman is cautious, he doesn't want to let it go. But when he sees Wanda's face flushing with emotion and her hands reaching out for the briefcase as she stammers, "There's blood...," he gives it to her.

Perhaps by way of apology for taking Karol's absence so lightly, one of the tenants says that before, when Karol's father was alive, everything went like clockwork. But ever since Mr. Wojtyla died, the boy was never home. He would come in and then disappear again. No one knew where he went, where or what he ate — how he lived, that is.

Wanda opens the briefcase. Out comes a loaf of bread wrapped in newspaper, two books covered with heavy black paper of the kind used on windows for blackouts, and a notebook whose pages are filled with thick notes. Wanda opens the books. One is *Pan Tadeusz* by Mickiewicz; in the margins, handwritten notes for direction. Between two pages is a sheet of paper, the confession of Jacek Soplica, copied by hand. The other book, to the girl's amazement, is a book on theology, The workman sees how surprised she is and says, "He was studying that book every chance he got. He used to ask me to let him into the stockroom. I'd let him in and he would read there and — how can I describe it? And he would pray. Yes, pray. On his knees, like in church. When I saw him the first time, I thought he was a little touched. But he wasn't. On the contrary. Too bad! He wasn't like the others."

Loudly, the woman tenant demands to know what happened to him. It may have been an accident, the workman says. Hopefully, nothing serious. Perhaps they should check the emergency ward or the hospital.

Wanda, on whose shoulders Marian rests his hands affectionately, has been listening to the workman's words with the briefcase tightly pressed to her chest. For her it is a completely new story, the story of a man who is a complete stranger to her.

The three friends rush to the hospital and go straight up to the men's ward. A sister in a white stand-out cowl takes them to a bed where a young man is lying, his head completely bandaged.

His face, covered with bandages, is unrecognizable. Wanda kneels at his bedside, clutching the briefcase in her hands.

"Will he live?" Marian asks, upset.

"It is all in the hands of God," answers the sister.

"Let us not disturb him, let him rest," says Marian.

"Yes, it is better," the sister remarks.

And Wanda, handing her the priescase, whispers:

"Excuse me, sister; when he awakes, will you give him this?..."

Then they leave together, while Wanda, wrapt in thought, murmurs a poem on the sorrow in human destiny.

It is late and the young people have to get back to the Baudienst dormitory. Marian says he has to stop off at his parents' house. Wanda asks Tadek if he must do the same, but he says no, he has already done so. Marian gives him an ironic look, as if to say, "Liar!" But Tadek, ignoring him says, "I'll go with you."

The three of them start walking toward the house together, then Marian, quickening his step, goes on ahead leaving Tadek with Wanda. But she doesn't say a word the whole way. When they get to the house she offers Tadek her hand and says thank you. Tadek says shyly:

"I'd like, once more —."

"You can come to next week's show," Wanda says.

"But I, I'd like to see you."

Wanda isn't listening. She doesn't answer and goes into the building.

TADEUSZ AND JOSEF'S ESCAPE

The persecution of the Jews, one of the most maniacal aspects of Nazism, began some years before World War II: round-ups, raids, mass deportations, concentration camps for forced labor and extermination. It was a methodical, progressive, blanket operation that extended through all the territories under the direct or indirect control of Hitler's Reich. As a temporary alternative, there was the ghetto. All the Jews of the city were forced to resettle in a neighborhood chosen by the authorities. In this walled area the Jews lived isolated and in miserable conditions under the continuous threat of deportation.

On April 14, 1943 the Warsaw ghetto rose, but the heroic gesture ended in a slaughter and the total destruction of the ghetto. Consequently other ghettos were disbanded. The Jews who were judged fit were sent to labor camps; the others were murdered on the spot — the elderly, the women, the children, the infants and the new-born.

The Cracow ghetto suffered the same fate. First invaded on January 18, 1943, it was destroyed on May 16 after the strenuous resistance to the German attack initiated on April 19.

At the end of the operation, while platoons of SS and gendarmes still surrounded the ghetto with rifles drawn to finish up any survivors, the men of the Baudienst were called to remove the corpses from the houses and streets and to clean up the rubble and debris.

With the Vorarbeiter (squad leaders) in black overalls and caps and the building squads in their blue uniforms and gray berets, the operation begins at dawn and lasts all day. The streets of the ghetto look dead, doors and windows are wide open. Here and there a curtain sways gently in the breeze, but everywhere on the walls and casings are black char spots from the fires, while in the streets, in the square, and in the lobbies and courtyards of the houses, are messy piles of household effects, boxes, suitcases, pillows and ripped mattresses from which feathers drift eerily through the neighborhood that has been reduced to a cemetery.

Gendarmes and police inspect the streets and houses looking for precious objects, kicking their way through the enormous garbage heaps of goods and corpses. "Get his manure out of here!" an SS officer orders the Baudienst men. Immediately the Vorarbeiter, with loud commands, split the column up into groups, one for the furniture, one for the bodies, one to burn rags and paper. *Ein, zwei, drei* — move!

Tadeusz and Marian are assigned to the bodies. Their route takes them through courtyards and alleyways, brokendown doors and destroyed apartments. It throws them into deepest despair. They work silently, without exchanging glances, dragging mutilated bodies into the street. The cadavers are lined up on the sidewalks and from there, piled up on trucks.

Suddenly Tadeusz can stand no more. He leans back, shoulders hunched, against a wall in the hallway of a home that has been sacked. He breaks out in a cry of rebellion and raging disgust. Marian jumps at him and covers his mouth with his cap.

"Let me yell or I'll go crazy!" Tadek says, pushing him away.

"Pray!" Marian suggests.

"I can't. We are at the bottom of hell. God can't hear us down here."

"We're at the top of Golgotha."

"But it is a Golgotha without Christ. And without meaning."

A Vorarbeiter, seeing them idle in the hallway, shouts, "Work, work! Do you want to go to Auschwitz?"

"You see? There are deeper depths to this hell," Marian murmurs. And he goes out into the street. Tadek moves to follow him. But he sees that the Vorarbeiter's back is turned, and struck by a sudden impulse, he goes back inside, swiftly climbs the stairs and enters one of the sacked apartments where the windows are still covered with thick black paper. The floor is littered with torn Hebrew books, and family photographs hang sadly from the walls. And like a hunted animal he seeks refuge in the kitchen.

Desperate, he is crouching on a stool, his head in his hands, when he hears a groan from under a table.

"Who is it?" Tadeusz asks.

"Josef Dajches," comes the fearful answer.

Quickly Tadek lifts the table and helps up an emaciated, starving young man, dressed in rags. He is an old acquaintance, nicknamed Jozek, but Tadek can hardly recognize him. The young man can't remember how long it has been since he has eaten. Everyone is gone. He is hiding, waiting his turn. In his pocket Tadek has a piece of black bread. He gives it to the young Jew, who devours it greedily. When the bread is gone, Jozek begs, "Don't turn me in. We've known one another for some time. Go. Leave me in peace."

"I'm hiding, too. If I go back now they'll send me to Auschwitz, and that'll be the end of me, too," Tadeusz says.

"But why are you hiding?" Jozek asks. "You can get out of the Baudienst, but you can't get out of here."

"I couldn't take anymore," Tadek answers.

Josek's eyes close as he relives the past few days and he says, "You haven't seen anything yet. At least it's quiet now."

Tadek suggests that Jozek run away withhim. The young man is incredulous, but Tadek insists. He asks him how far the wall is from the house. "It's behind the courtyard," Jozek answers.

"We'll jumpt it," Tadek says, offering his hand. Jozek tells him that there is actually an opening in the wall, which is why he has been hiding. He was waiting for the right moment but was afraid to come out. And hunger had held him back. When Tadeusz realizes that the opening leads to the rocks behind Saint Joseph's Church, he doesn't hesitate.

"Let's go," he says to Jozek.

"Think it over carefully," his friend answers. "You have a lot more to loose than I."

Saint Joseph's Church, which stands on the low slope of Krzemionki Hill, faces Podgorski Square. There are few in attendance at evening prayers. In the weak candlelight the rosary is recited before the Holiest Sacrament on the altar in preparation for the eucharistic blessing. It is a daily rite that the bishops have requested to pray for peace. The prayer is being recited in two voices between the altar and the nave when Tadek and Jozek come through the front entrance, compose themselves hurriedly, and sit down in one of the darker pews. For a moment they are safe, but their hearts are beating wildly and they are panting. They whisper to one another. Tadek is confident, Jozek pessimistic.

"You see? We're alive."

"It's true. But who's going to hide a Jew? Who's going to risk his life for him?"

"No one wants to die. But to help, yes. Wait!"

Tadek approaches a confessional where he has seen a stout, middle-aged priest in surplice and stole reading his breviary. Tadek begins with the usual words, "Christ be praised," but quickly he comes to the point. He is not there to confess. He is from the Baudienst, he has escaped from the ghetto duty bringing with him a Jewish friend who was hiding.

The priest turns out the light and is silent. Tadek asks for help. His voice trembling, he says he cannot abandon his friend. If he were to be killed and Tadek were saved, he would feel remorse for the rest of his life.

"Lower your voice. Let me think. Where is he?"

"Sitting in one of the pews near the choir box."

"All right then, listen carefully. Stay where you are until the church closes. I'll tell the sacrestan not to bother you. Wait for me there. Now go back to him, for he must not be afraid of anything. I'll give you my blessing, then I'll knock on the door of the confessional as usual so as not to arouse suspicion. But remember, when this is over, come to confession. *Benedicat te omnipotens Deus, Pater et Filius et Spiritus Sanctus.*"

With his knuckles he raps on the door while Tadek rises and returns to his pew. Just then the organ sounds the *Tantum ergo*, then comes the benediction between the tolling of the bells and the swinging of the incense burners by the choirboys in their picturesque robes. At last the celebrant, a young man about the same age as the other two, goes through the church sprinkling holy water on the worshippers. A last ray of sunlight coming in through the windows makes the holy water shine like pearls in the air.

So that no one on his way out will notice them, the two young men crouch down in the pew and wait until the church is closed and silence has returned.

Shortly afterward, the young priest appears near the altar. He approaches quickly and in a whisper tells the men to follow him. He walks along the side nave, toward the sacristy.

By now it is almost night. From the priest's house perched on the gentle slope of the Krzemionki, the young priest appears and looks around. He returns the respectful wave of a passerby and checks to be sure that the coast is clear. Then he goes back inside. Three priests walk in front of the house.

34

The parish priest is the stout older man from the confession. On either side of him are two younger clerics in cassocks with black capes on their shoulders and wide-brimmed hats on their heads. He tells them what to do. They are to take a tram at the stop on Kalwaryiska Street, ride to the end of the line, and go from there to the nearby Borek train station. Before they leave, he traces the sign of the cross on their foreheads, then gives them a gentle push. Finally he goes back inside the entranceway and watches them through the half-open door.

Tadeusz and Josef walk along with a natural air despite their unusual garments. They are already some distance away when the priest tells the young vicar to run after them. He has forgotten something. Priests never go anywhere with empty hands. He looks around, takes a black bag from the coatrack and an umbrella and tells him to give one to Josef and the other to Tadek. The young vicar objects: "But the bag is mine!"

"And the umbrella is mine," says the older man. "Now they'll really look like two priests!"

Since the tram comes from the direction of the ghetto, Josef looks that way. But Tadek discourages him. It is dangerous to show any interest. The first tram car is completely empty; it is the one reserved for the Germans according to the sign in big letters: "Nur fur Deutsche." The second car reads the opposite: "Fur Nichtdeutsche," for non-Germans. The two "priests" can hardly squeeze onto the rear platform. Little by little, however, passengers get off, and near Mateczne Tadek and Josef are able to enter the car. A young worker, a book in his hand, sees them and rises politely to give them his seat.

Tadek, nearly ecstatic at the nearness of their destination, begins to play the part of priest and says with a protective air, "God bless you, my son! But stay seated. What happened, have you had an accident?" The young man is wearing a bandage on his head. In spite of the priest's refusal, he prefers to remain standing. As for the bandage, he says, "It's an old story. It's nothing." And hanging on to the overhead strap, his hand raised, he goes back to the book he is holding in his other hand. The book is covered with heavy black paper.

Tadek sits down and makes himself comfortable, his hands resting on the umbrella, his legs crossed. Josef, in front of him, sits on the edge of the seat and casts worried glances around him from under the brim of his hat. Tadek, happy, whistles.

A voice whispers, "Don't whistle, and don't cross your legs. A real priest doesn't behave that way."

He raises his eyes, astonished. The young worker is still standing there reading. Tadek does as he's told and stretches his robe out over his feet.

The voice says, "Tell your friend to stop looking around. He should stare at the toes of his shoes, like a real priest."

The worker heads toward the exit.

"Solvay!" the conduc or announces as the tram stops.

OPPRESSION AND RESISTANCE

Nazism allows for no forgiveness, only punishment and reprisals. Tadek's escape backfires heavily on his friend Marian. The SS takes him in for questioning and tortures him. Where has his friend gone? They were together in the Baudienst. In the dormitory their cots were next to one another. They were together in the ghetto during the clean-up operation. He must know, he must say.

"He walked away a moment, then he disappeared. Maybe a wall caved in on him. I don't know what happened."

The soldier beats him with a billy-blub on the head and back. He screams and faints. A bucket of ice water is poured over his head to revive him. The SS officer questioning him knows perfectly well that Marian has no idea what has happened, but he doesn't care. Bored, he watches the soldier work the victim over. Then he makes the usual decision: destination Auschwitz. That way others will think twice before they decide to slip away.

Marian, transferred to Auschwitz, is now a number in a striped cotton uniform, his head shaved and covered with a cap. He is pushed into a barracks, registered, assigned a place, a miserable bunk that is one of the hundreds upon hundreds built on wooden stilts in the immense room.

He lies down hesitantly next to a hefty man who doesn't even bother

37

looking at him. It is the time for silence, but light sighs are to be heard everywhere in the barracks.

His neighbor says only, "Have you anything to eat?"

"No, nothing."

The silence that ensues seems to say, "Then you're worthless."

Marian needs to communicate and says to the man, "I was in the Baudienst, a friend of mine ran away, and they arrested me. My family has no idea where I am. If they knew they'd get me out. It's not my fault my friend ran away."

His answer is silence. Anguished, Marian is unable to sleep. He tosses and turns on his straw bed and in the half-light he sees the entire room with its living dead defeated by exhaustion, hunger and misery. Near his stack of bunks, kneeling with hands folded, is an emaciated prisoner, stock-still.

"Look!" he says to his neighbor, touching him.

The man turns around, annoyed, and when he has seen the kneeling man, turns over again and tries to sleep.

"Who is he!" asks Marian.

"A man."

"A priest?"

"There was a priest. He volunteered to die in exchange for that one's life. And that one kneels and prays all night long."

Marian lies immobile on his bunk, his eyes wide open. At one point he touches his neighbor's shoulder, but the man ignores him.

Dawn has already broken over the spires of the Kalwaria sanctuary. In the courtyard of the monastery a Francescan monk is chopping wood. Another is leading a horse from the stall and hitching it to a buggy. Father Marek arrives, a crown of white hair around his shaven head. He carries a bundle which he tosses into the back of the buggy. He and the monk in charge of the horse look around carefully, then go back to the stall while the animal eats from a feedbag attached to the wall. The horse's tail switches at flies. The woodchopping monk keeps an eye on the situation. The two monks leave the stall with a big, low crate and place it under the buggy seat. Father Marek climbs aboard, takes the reins and with a crack of the whip at the horse's flanks, sets out toward the monastery gates.

"In the name of God!" his helper shouts in a parting salute.

Two priests in cassocks and black capes, wearing wide hats with the brims pulled low over their faces, are waiting outside. They are Tadek and Josef. Around them several worshippers are arriving for mass. No bells ring.

It is silent by order of Archbishop Sapieha as a sign of mourning. The two men look worried, but as soon as they spot the buggy they go forward it and quickly board, sitting on the bench behind Father Marek, and their trip begins.

The road from the monastery toward town goes up a steep hill and comes out in market square. Suddenly two gendarmes order the buggy to a halt. Father Marek, reins and whip in hand and a friendly smile on his face, listens to their questions.

"Where are so many priests headed?'

"Wadowice, for the feast of Saint Michael."

"My name's Michael, too."

"God bless you."

The gendarme touches the bundle with the rod of his machine gun. "What's this?"

Father Marek unties the bundle. Inside are liturgical vestments for the mass and other trappings, including a chalice and gold paten.

"What's this?" the gendarme asks suspiciously. "Don't they have this stuff in Wadowice?" He reaches to touch it, but Father Marek pulls the things toward himself indigaantly.

"You can't do that!"

"All right, all right," says the gendarme, confused.

But the other man, who hasn't taken his eyes of Jozek the whole time, is also suspicious and interrupts.

"One moment. Your papers."

Jozek begins slowly unbuttoning his cassock to get to his wallet when Father Marek distracts everyone by exclaiming, "What is that infernal rumpus?"

A mighty rumble of engines draws nearer. People rush into their doorways, the peasants pull their carts off the road, and in the distance a platoon of soldiers on motorcycles appears followed by a small truck with an officer waving a signal flag. Immediately behind him comes a column of gigantic Waffen-SS, the enemy tanks. The two gendarmes hurry to clear the road and Father Marek wastes no time — with a flick of his whip, the horse is off at a gallop toward the military column. When it is near the first motorcycles, Marek pulls at the reins and the buggy turns down a sidestreet and is lost in a cloud of dust.

Tadeusz and Josef can hardly manage to keep their seats in the rocking buggy, and under the straw the big crate full of weapons slides around.

At the edge of the forest in the gamekeeper's hut, Father Marek is saying his rosary, seated on a chest, while Tadek and Josef nap on a wooden bench. They have loosened their cassocks and feel safe, closer to freedom.

The gamekeeper, with his fur-lined leather vest and his pipe in his mouth, surveys the woods through the windows. When he hears a dog bark he says:

"They're coming!"

The four stand up and group together in front of the window. The figures of armed men can be seen advancing from the forest. They are partisans dressed in worn clothing and armed in a wide variety of ways. With extreme caution they are led, in single file, by a sturdy man whose cheek is disfigured by a deep scar and whose cap bears the rank of junior officer. He is their leader, Wladek Zapala.

The partisans enter the room. Wladek greets Father Marek:

"Christ be praised."

"Hurry!" the priest answers. "An SS tank column was on its way to Wadowice today."

They all run toward the buggy, which is stopped in front of the hut. Tadeusz and Josef, who have removed their cassocks in the meantime, run with them.

"Who are these men?" Wladek asks suspiciously in front of the two priests who have turned into laymen.

"Volunteers, Sargeant," says Father Marek good-naturedly.

"But we haven't enough provisions or weapons."

"Listen, my son, one of them escaped from the ghetto, the other from the Baudienst. When we left Kalwaria, the gendarmes had their eyes on them. What else can we do?"

Wladek pulls Father Marek aside by his sleeve. "Father, how are things at my home?"

"The women are taking care of the farm, the boy is growing up."

"Has he really grown?"

"In no time I'll bring him here to you as a partisan. Come, let's get on with it."

The column leaves, carrying the crate of weapons. Father Marek follows along after them with his bundle of stuff for the mass. The dog pulls angrily at its chain as the gamekeeper's eyes follow the men moving farther into the distance.

In a forest clearing under the warm autumn sun the partisan unit gathers around a makeshift altar. They are without weapons, their caps in hand as they follow, in deep silence, the mass Father Marek is celebrating for them.

40

The red chasuble stands out against the green of the trees and the brown of the trunks that form the altar, while the gold chalice shines in the sun at the moment of elevation. Before the raised chalice the partisans kneel. Suddenly there is a sharp explosion and a red rocket blazes over the clearing. Wladek gives the signal coldly:

"Emergency!"

Word passes from mouth to mouth and the men begin disbanding rapidly but in an orderly fashion. One group runs to the ditches where the weapons are hidden, others smother the fires and cover the camp stoves and ditches with branches. Father Marek finishes his prayers, kisses the altar and raises his hands:

"*Benedicat vos omnipotens Deus....*"

He turns to give his blessing. Before him the clearing is deserted. He continues with a wide gesture of his hands:

"*Pater et Filius et Spiritus Sanctus....*"

At that very moment an explosion at the center of the clearing sends up black smoke that covers the altar, the priest and the woods where the partisans are hiding. A German plane flies low over the area.

A small German convoy is coming down one of the roads that runs alongside the wood. In the lead is a man on a motorcycle wearing a helmet and behind him comes a line of trucks carrying men. The partisans have stretched a steel cable across the road; it blends in among the trees. The cyclist runs into it, is thrown from his seat and is run over by the first truck. To avoid a pile-up the second truck winds up off the road. Simultaneously the partisans open fire from invisible positions, concentrating all their fire on the convoy and rendering resistance impossible. The Germans, jumping down from the trucks, defend themselves well, but they are outdone.

Only corpses are left on the ground. Then the partisans hasten to the spot, and horse-drawn wagons appear out of the bushes. The men load the weapons, boots, blankets, food supplies and anything else they can carry onto the wagons, which set off again as soon as possible into the forest.

A wounded German officer tries to escape into the forest. Wladek Zapala follows him. When the man falls, Zapala takes the pistol that he is holding in his fist. Then, seeing that the man is dying, he finishes him off. War hardens men's souls. Wladek observes the officer, hesitates a moment, then pulls off the man's leather boots and his own boots and tries on the new pair. Quickly he orders his men to retreat. They gather at a spot just above the path. Among them are Tadek and Josef, excited by their baptism by fire. Shortly afterward the men disappear into the woods, carrying their wounded.

CONVULSIONS AT WAR'S END

On Franciszkanska Street is the Archbishop's Palace, residence of Prince Adam Stefan Sapieha, the spiritual head of the metropolitan archdiocese of Cracow. But the palace is also the moral landmark of the entire Polish people, a people deprived for years of their Cardinal, Archbishop Augusto Hlond of Gniezno, who has been deported to Germany. Nearby is the headquarters of the gendarme, where citizens arrested in police dragnets are brought. Traffic on the street is heavy. Trucks arrive loaded with people and depart empty. The rumble of engines filters through the thick walls of the archbishopric.

It is Wednesday, August 2, 1944. The Archbishop is in his chapel finishing his morning prayers. He is on his knees, but his back is straight, his eyes raised to the cross. The door of the chapel opens slowly and on tip-toe the vicar of the cathedral approaches Monsignor Sapieha.

"Radio London has just announced that an uprising has broken out in Warsaw. Fighting has been going on since yesterday. There is a lot of movement going on here at German police headquarters. They must be preparing for something."

The Archbishop doesn't move, he doesn't take his eyes off the cross.

"Excellency, I must add that the gentleman you have been waiting for is here."

43

Show him in. And be careful of the boys. Don't let them leave the building."

With a military stride, a colonel of the National Secret Army enters. His bearing is erect. He is dressed in civilian clothes, but he wears officer's boots and carries a jacket of military cut. He greets the Archbishop with dignity and respect, then, at his host's invitation, sits down on a chair next to a table at one side of the altar.

"Excellency, we're at the finish line," he says. "The Soviets are marching all along the front. Warsaw has risen. Now it's our turn."

"What does that mean?" Sapieha asks in a stony voice.

"That we wish to take part in the action by declaring an uprising in Cracow as well. My job is to inform your Excellency."

The Archbishop is silent and the colonel, puzzled, asks:

"What is your Excellency's opinion?"

Articulating every word, Sapieha answers, "I am not a soldier. I am thinking only of where to provide for the wounded and the fugitives. But we have plenty of churches, convents and palaces still empty. We'll make them available. And our priests, nuns and clerics as well. That's all."

"No, that's not all. We would like a proclamation from Your Excellency."

"No," the Archbishop answers decisively.

"Why not?"

"I can only do my duty as pastor. I collect and protect my flock, I do not send it to slaughter."

With a bow, the colonel takes his leave.

The Archbishop is alone. He kneels again before the tabernacle and hides his face in his hands.

Sounds of police trucks echo through the walls.

In that month of August 1944 the fate of the Axis seemed sealed. After the successes of the first years of war, made possible in part by the Soviet-German Pact of August 22, 1939, things began to change rapidly. Hitler's massive attack against the USSR, which began on June 22, 1941, bled the Reich's armies white and marked the turning point in the war, beginning from the German surrender at Stalingrad on February 2, 1943. During that year German resistance to the Allied offensive still seemed possible. But those hopes diminished in 1944. Heroic actions began then, such as the Warsaw revolt against the Germans, begun on August 1 and lasting until October 3, while the Soviets, reaching the eastern shores of the Vistola on

44

August 31, halted their advanced. Under those circumstances, German repression grew sharper.

Cracow was sifted through. On August 6, a hot day that was to go down in history as "Black Sunday," a German army appeared in the city and began hunting men down. All males were to be captured. People fled, seeking refuge where they could. But the police were at their heels. They broke down doors, invaded buildings, snatched half-stunned men, many of them on their way back from the country or an excursion or a day's fishing, and others — those who had remained in the city — dressed in their light summer clothes. There was no way to resist, not with arguments, nor documents, nor by force. Hundreds of trucks brought in as reinforcements for the garrison loaded thousands of citizens and took them far away. The city reverberated with the deafening sounds of engines. Everywhere were the cries of women, the despair of families.

The trucks roll down Franciszkanska Street beneath the windows of the Archbishop's Palace. Near dusk, Adam Stefan Sapieha stands hands folded at the window. He watches the anguished city falling prey to panic and desperation. Behind him are the otherpriests, among them the vicar of the cathedral. The Archbishop says to them:

"Tomorrow you will fetch all the students of the clandestine faculty, in addition to the group that is already here with us. We are formally re-opening the seminary."

They could arrest the rector," says the vicar of the cathedral.

"I will be the rector. Let them take me." Then after a pause, "Everyone should wear the cassock. Make sure you collect enough of them. Take yours, take mine, too..."

"Where are we going to put the students?"

"Here, in my house," says Sapieha, and he gestures broadly around him to take in the reception hall where they stand.

A group of clerics, some already wearing habits of odd sizes, others in civilian clothes — mostly in shirtsleeves — work in the reception room of the Archbishopric. They are removing the antique furniture, taking paintings off the walls. Then they bring in iron cots, straw mattresses, stools, basins. The hall is gradually transformed into a dormitory.

The vicar of the cathedral is walking down Tyniecka Street and stops at number ten. He goes down into the sub-basement and knocks on a modest door. He waits with some apprehension and then, with relief, hears the

45

sound of footsteps. The door opens and young Karol Wojtyla appears. His face is shadowed because no light filters down from the dark landing above. The vicar is visible in the light coming from the room. His message is simple: "Praise Christ. Come. The Metropolitan awaits you. Take your cassock because from now on you stay with us."

The clandestine student of Polish literature, who has for some time been a clandestine student of theology as well, becomes, from that August 1944 on, part of the group of seminarians preparing for the priesthood under the protection of Archbishop Sapieha. From that moment on all his friends will know of the young man's true intention.

On January 13, 1945 the winter offensive of the Soviet army began. On January 17 the Red Army entered Warsaw, on January 19 Cracow and Lodz. In Warsaw they found only ruins. Twenty thousand of the resistance and two hundred thousand civilians died during the uprising; fifteen thousand were taken prisoners, and seven hundred thousand civilians were deported. The city was then systematically destroyed. Cracow, on the other hand, was found virtually intact.

Nevertheless, the Germans took with them on their retreat many prisoners and hostages, especially prisoners from the concentration camp at Auschwitz.

DRAMA OF THE WAR'S AFTERMATH

It is spring day in 1945. The concentration camp, Mauthausen, in northwestern Austria, has been liberated by the allied forces. The prisoners in the camp wear used American uniforms which have been supplied by the United Nations Relief and Rehabilitation Administration, the international organization founded by the United Nations in 1943 to provide economic and civic assistance for war-torn nations. People can finally breathe easier.

Marian, who has been transported here by the Germans, is wrapping his possession into a bundle. His old bunkmate, who has lived through the same ordeal, is watching him, his eyes vacant.

"So, goodbye — you're going back to Poland?" he says to Marian, offering his hand. "To do what?" he murmurs.

Marian looks at him, hesitating, and finally turns to leave. But the other calls him back.

"Hey, you! Wait! Write me, will you," he adds timidly. "Let me know how things are going."

"But I'm not going back right away. I want to travel around. I'm going to Rome."

"Rome? What for?"

"I want to see if it's still standing. If Rome isn't destroyed, Cracow can't be."

Marian arrives in the Rome train station wearing half an American Army uniform, a skullcap, and carrying a bundle in his hand. He heads directly for Saint Peter's Square, and arrives as a solemn celebration, led by Pius XII, is coming to an end. He sees the papal procession passing: Swiss guards in full uniform, pontifical officials, Palatine and Noble guards, prelates, protonotaries, Capitolari from Saint Peter's, Bishops, Archbishops, Cardinals, all in the pomp and flashing color of their uniforms. The Pope presides high above them on the gestatorial chair. Carried by the grooms, surrounded by great ostrich feathers, he passes with the cape around his shoulders and crown on his head to greet and bless the faithful. As the Pontiff greets them, the crowds cheer and kneel before him. Marian removes his skullcap and kneels.

When the ceremony is over, more dazed than impressed, the young man wanders out to the square, walks toward one of the huge fountains, and sits down on the edge of the iron railing that surrounds it. Lost in thought, he hears a grating voice ask:

"Auschwitz?"

Spinning around quickly, he sees a priest only a little older than himself.

He nods yes, unwillingly, irritated at hearing the name of the camp spoken in perfect German. The priest understands the young man's reaction and immediately explains that he is, in fact, German. But then, lifting the sleeve of his cassock, he displays a number tatooed on his forearm. The two compare numbers; the priest's is lower.

"I was put away before the war. What about you?"

"Right afterwards, but in Poland."

"Really? What are you doing here?"

"I don't know. I'd like to erase all this by traveling around the world," he says, holding out his arm. "I don't want to go home like this."

"Dedicate yourself to studying," the priest advises warmly. "Learn to do something you were doing before. Or try to do something you didn't know before. Like me. I've come back here to complete the studies I'd begun before I was arrested."

"Before?" Marian shakes his head. "Before I was just a boy. Now I'm a prisoner. How can I learn to be a man?"

"You are of the chosen," the priest insists, "because you escaped extermination. The whole human race is like Noah's progeny. Blessed by divine grace. Just think, we were both there. Two numbers and now we're here in this sacred spot, the heart of the church."

Marian feels anger starting.

48

"We'd have to destroy this Basilica and build a new one, but not here. Over there, in the Piazza Appello."

"Even this Basilica was built on the bones of the martyrs," answers the priest. "Above an Auschwitz of two thousand years ago. Don't forget that God lives in the condemned man, in the prisoner. The instrument of torture and death is our symbol. We, dear friend, are at home. The church is our only true home."

"With all that pomp?"

"Listen," says the other, smiling. "When we were all smiling standing during the ceremony I kept asking myself if I could watch all this again, if I could listen again to the chorus of the Sistine Chapel. And I forced myself to imagine it. I forced myself to listen. Isn't it a miracle that all of this has remained? That all this could last in time? We understand this better than anybody else. We came from so far away."

Then he slapped Marian on the shoulder.

"Go back to your country. You'll find something worthy of being loved there."

Following the Allies' conferences of 1945 (Yalta, January 2-12; Potsdam, August 1), the Poland on the geographical map underwent a huge transformation. Its territory was reduced and was, so to speak, put on kilometers from east to west. In the East, the ancient cities of Velno and Leopoli were lost with all their geographic hinterlands. The boundary line between the Soviet Union and Poland was established along the Bug River. In the West, once Polish territories which had been part of Germany were returned and the line of demarcation with the future German Democratic Republic was established along the Rivers Oddie and Nassie. Millions of men — Russians, Poles and Germans — gave their lives to one of the greatest migrations in history. For Poles and Germans it was a matter of forced migration which compelled them to leave the beloved land they'd inhabited for generations and venture toward the unknown to remake their lives.

A train of immigrants, going from the territories into the Soviet Union, moves along the areas abandoned by the Germans which now make up Western Poland. The overworked convoy is decorated with flags and banners praising the homecoming. But on the freight and livestock cars, where each person has loaded all that he owns, from fine furniture to cattle, the dominant emotion is one of sadness. People watch the unknown landscape apprehensively.

Marian is on the train as a functionary of the Polish government. He wears a red and white armband with the letters PVR (Office of Polish Repatriation). He moves about gracefully, informing people, trying to solve their various problems. He is likeable and people feel warmly toward him.

One one car, an old ailing priest is lying on a wornout blanket spread on the floor. He holds to him the sacred image of the child Jesus, clothed in colorful clothes, common in the Slavic tradition.

"How are you feeling, Father," asks Marian.

"If only we'd get there. Are we almost there?"

"Normally the whole trip would take a few hours," answers Marian. "But now it's as if we have to cross the ocean. The track is blocked or the locomotive breaks down or they've given other trains the go ahead."

After thinking a moment, the priest continues:

"I'm lying here thinking: What was God's lesson in shunting us around here? After all we've already gone through."

"And who knows that the good God whishes to say to us!," Marian answers him, following the line of his thoughts. "Well, I would have liked the Church to have condemned Nazism more forcefully — for example... I don't know... an excommunication for the concentration camps. Why didn't she do it?"

"I only know, whispers the priest, that God, provides and enlightens, and that we are not always able to understand him."

"That, Father, is what you can tell the people at the first mass." "Why do you think there's a church there?"

"If there isn't, we'll build one."

The old priest, shaking his head, adds, "It will not be me. I'm a tree from my homeland. An old, worm-eaten tree, broken by years of work. They're taking me there to transplant me, to give us all the illusion that this is the same land we were nourished on, raised on. Good Lord, how the poor people have suffered."

These last words are meant as an aside to God or even a reproach to Marian, who represents the authority. In any case, Marian grasps the priest's arm to comfort him. As he is about to walk away, the priest detains him.

"And you. Will you stay there with us?"

"No, I really can't," he says, shaking his head. "I don't think I'll be settling anywhere. It's the success of Auschwitz."

When the train arrives, cars jolting, the people are reduced to bare nerves. The courageous among them enter the abandoned houses. Marian helps the old and the children. He tries to keep order.

There's also a church, but it's an Evangelical one, cold and strangely

50

different from the Catholic church they've left behind. The door is wide open. Some are willing to carry the statue of Jesus inside along with a painting of the Madonna of Ostra Brama, the sanctuary in Vilno. They are placed on the altar, as the onlookers kneel and pray silently.

Suddenly, gun shots echo, followed by cries of terror. The people leap up and run. An old German is barricaded in one of the houses and has decided to defend his property. When the Polish peasants tried to force open the courtyard gate, he fired.

Marian orders the people to stay back. Then he raises his hands to his mounth and shouts in German:

"Throw out the gun. Come out. We won't hurt you."

Shortly afterward, the old man comes out slowly and Marian protects him from the furious crowd of peasants who threaten to lynch him. The church is the only refuge. The priest takes the German inside to protect him, repeating wisely to his people:

"Don't kill him."

Sunday arrives and the people congregate for mass in the well-cleaned church, decorated with flowers and pine branches. Marian enters the sacristy and finds the old parish priest dressed in his liturgical vestments, collapsed in a chair. He feels exhausted and cannot fin the strength to go to the altar.

"What will happen if I die? What will become of them? Who will help them? Who will understand them? My son, give me absolution."

Marian is dismayed. Already the faithful have been waiting too long. They have gone through all the songs and primary prayers. To ease the tension, he appears at the doors of the sacristy and rings the bell announcing the beginning of mass. In relief, the people rise to their feet and wait. Even the old curate has found the strength and with the chalice in his hand, makes his way toward the altar.

Cracow celebrates. Not only have the Germans left, but the war is over. There are signs of war everywhere: bunkers, fortifications, barricades. The invaders had hoped they would serve a resistance which could have meant the city's destruction. But now they're covered with streamers and posters announcing the defeat of the Third Reich and the reaction to it. The red and white national flags which had been hidden away in the most remote corners of the houses are now fluttering from the balconies. The citizens are wearing rosettes, red and white armbands and badges with the Polish crowned eagle.

The city is full of military men: Russians, Poles and ex-partisans. Prisoners of war are coming home. Political prisoners are coming home.

Tadeusz and Josef have come home, too, bearing scars from the clandestine war — they wear boots and military shirts, their beards are long, their skin darkened by the sun, their glances full of mistrust, ready for any assault. They stop near the university, where a crowd of students wearing brand-new university hats are gathering.

"Now what are we supposed to do?" asks Josef.

"I'm going to register in the university," says Tadeusz.

"I want to try my hand at the pen. I think I have a story to tell. But I want to go home now, to see my parents."

"Sure, go ahead."

Tadeusz suddenly remembers that Josef has no family left. He takes him by the arm.

"Come with me. My family will treat you like a son."

"No, thanks. I'm going to look for a place to stay and a job. I can't write, I'm not cut out for studying, there's no future here for business, and I've had it up to here with the military. Politics is where I want to be. It seems the power has been left out on the streets. I'm going to try to grab it."

"Just don't fall in the sewer. Good luck, Jozek."

As Tadek and Jozek shake hands and say their goodbyes, Tadek suddenly notices someone pass. He pulls his hand away from Jozek's and begins to run.

He has seen Wanda walking thoughtfully along the main path in the Planty Garden, carrying a sign. He walks up to her without a word and falls into step alongside her.

"Oh, it's you. How unexpected," Wanda says to him, stopping in surprise.

"And how aggressive of me. Otherwise I wouldn't have dared to approach you."

"What are you doing?" she asks, hurrying onward.

"I've just gotten back from the war. And you're the first familiar face I saw. Where are you going?"

"To the theater, as usual."

"The same theater?"

"The same old theater. I don't change my ways."

"But I do. And that guy (and he circles his head with a hand as if to wrap it in a bandage), did he ever get better?"

"He's all better. There's not even a mark. He's about to be ordained as a priest."

52

"No kidding!"

"He was already a clergyman. But he didn't say anything. Here we are."

"We're standing outside the Gestapo, if I'm not mistaken," says Tadek jokingly, raising his gaze toward the door where Wanda is heading.

"Precisely. But we're here to meditate. Now, let's meditate, here, with our professor who hasn't changed one bit. He's like he always was. He moves us around on the chessboard as he pleases. Do you want to see him? Do you want to try again?"

"No, no," says Tadek, rubbing his head. "I've lost my mind, too. But in an even worse way. Because something gave inside me. I'm looking for a reason to live. I'm looking for an explanation for what happened and for what can happen next."

"Couldn't we talk about it?" he asks, taking Wanda's hand.

"But we're here talking," she remarks, smiling.

"Talk to me seriously. I need it. I wanted to see you. Really wanted to see you. I tried to find you."

She answers soberly:

"He who seeks shall find. But you only came upon me, you didn't find me, not yet. He who seeks shall find — even your explanation of the past and your ideas about the future. I hope you find the right things. Goodbye, I'm in a rush."

And she slipped gracefully into the lobby of the building that was once the Gestapo's and now bore the inscription: Teatr Rapsodyczny (The Rhapsodic Theater).

Tadeusz went home to see his mother and father. The joy of the reunion, of knowing they were alive, was darkened by the deaths of his brothers in the war. And the poverty and misery which even a high school teacher like his father had to suffer saddened him. They had been forced to take refugees into their house, to share the kitchen and bedrooms. The foyer was full of suitcases and the furniture from other rooms; screens divided the living room into separate corners for each family.

During the next few days Tadeusz met Wanda in the city again. As always, their meeting was brief, but sufficient for the two to exchange their most important news. Tadeusz told Wanda that he planned to become a writer. After his experience in the war, he wanted to throw himself into this new occupation. Wanda, on the other hand, informed him that her brother Marian had left the Polish Repatriation Service to enter the seminary, along with Karol Wojtyla.

Bitterness and misunderstanding is most apparent at home. One day Tadek comes back to find his aging father, wearing his usual old suit from before the war, his old frayed shirt with its stiff collar, before a stack of papers to correct. He is run down, bent over.

"Thank goodness you're back. We're eating soon," his father tells him.

Tadek throws himself down on a bed behind the screen.

"Where's mother?"

"At church."

"At church all day?"

He looks around at the walls covered with sacred images and photographs taken at different times of all the children.

"It's an obsession. She wasn't like this before," he continues, exasperated.

His father answers wearily.

"Before — before there wasn't a war. We were all at home together."

"But I'm here. I came back. And mother hardly seems to notice. It's as though I were a stranger."

"You came back, but your brothers never will. Your mother looks at you in disbelief. She can't believe you're really here. That you're not really dead, too."

"But that's impossible. Mother's living in a dream. All Poland is living in a dream. All of Poland doubting that it's alive, not believing what's happening here today. As though none of it were true. But it is, it is."

He leaps up, lights a cigarette, puts it out on the partisan's boot, hardly aware that he's upset his father. And he continues talking to himself as the old professor goes into the kitchen.

"All of Poland is busy admiring little altars, little mementos. All of Poland crying and dreaming, unable to recognize its men. Like my mother."

His father brings him a bowl of soup and speaks livingly:

"Eat. It's the women who are paying the price of this war, more than anyone else. They have always paid — for the wars, the deportations, the insurrections. Their men are abducted, and they wait. They created the emotional history of our country. This is a country of mothers who suffer. And that is why we have a religion full of tenderness, and love, and apprehension. It's a religion of mothers. And our poetry is like that, too."

Tadek holds out his spoon, reflects for a moment and then blurts out:

"But a people of tearful mothers mourning sons cannot be. A nation of women! A nation of children!"

His father hears his wife come into the house. He is relieved.

54

"Here she comes now. Be kind to your mother."

When she comes in, she greets the two men and then reminds them quietly, straightforwardly, "Today is the feast of Wojtek." She takes the bunch of blessed flowers that she's brought from church and goes to place them next to the photograph of her oldest son.

Meanwhile another homecoming takes place in Kalwaria, on the hill where the sanctuary is. Wladek, the partisan leader, has left the woods and arms behind and returned to his home town. In his house he finds his mother, his wife, his son, Staszek, now grown up. His father, however, remained in Auschwitz, one of the many millions of victims of the occupation. He lost his life for having shot a pig illegally.

THE POSTWAR YEARS

The spring of 1946. Government authorities have forbidden the traditional celebration of May 3rd, commemorating the democratic constitution of 1791, the first one to be promulgated in Europe. It is also the national feast of the Madonna of Jasna Gora in Czestochowa, who was proclaimed the Queen of Poland by King John Casimiro in 1655. While Polish public opinion, in its huge majority, has loyalty to the West, the political power lies in the East. The new regime does not intend to tolerate opposition of any kind. Thus, the student protest over the canceled holiday has been answered by stringent repressive actions.

In Cracow the procession of students heads toward Rynek Glowny, the huge, splendid plaza in the marketplace. They were velvet university berets, carry national flags and march in files while chanting slogans in protest.

The file halts before Saint Mary's church. A restless crowd has gathered on all sides. And then suddenly the police rush in. Militiamen in light-green uniforms descend from several vans. They wear round, blue-striped caps and armbands inscribed with the letters MO, the initials of the territorial police, and they carry clubs. A little later the army joins them. Militiamen are stretched out on the hoods of vans their machine guns aimed at the crowd. The young people pretend not to notice the maneuvers closing in around them. A religious function is about to end inside the church. The singing, "God, may you protect Poland," can be heard in the plaza, and the youths and the crowd join in. Then the students begin moving again. They pass between the rows of men in uniform controlling the plaza, and then suddenly, in response to their leader's command, they begin running, pushing toward the vans, breaking through the soldiers' cordons. Slipping beneath the horses' bellies, they make for all the possible ways out and move away from Rynek Glowny to gather again in another part of the city. The people cheer them on. Flowers are thrown down on the protesters from the crowded windows where images of the Madonna of Czestochowa, the Polish insignia of the crowned eagle and portraits of Pilsudski and Kosciuszko are displayed. Notes of the patriotic hymns, "Hail, Dawn of May" and "Warszawianka" float up from the street.

Tadeusz, who is not among the protesters, stands on the sidewalk watching the procession. Suddenly he notices Wanda's face among the marching students. He bolts out toward the file and tries to catch up to the young woman, breaking through the chain of clasped hands. He shoves his way through, but two boys stop him, and taking him by the arm, push him back to another part of the file, warning him to keep in step with the others. At that moment, light cannons in armored cars fire at the head of the file. It is obvious that they are aiming directly for the front of the procession. To continue under such circumstances would be madness. The procession scatters all at once. The youths and the crowd flee toward the park, climbing over barbed-wire fences from wartime, leaping over the air-raid trenches. Some fall down, some hurt themselves. An armored car swerves during the maneuver, slams into a tree and knocks it down. Now the light cannons fire into the air. Polish and Soviet officials armed with pistols begin jumping from the cars. They command the troop in brief, simple terms, and pursue the young men and women fleeing. The hunt is on in all parts of the city.

Tadek catches up to Wanda, puts his arm around her and drags her to a side street. She shakes and cries.

"They aimed at the crowd, aimed —," she screams.

Archbishop Saphieha, recently named a Cardinal — he was nominated and the investiture met in Rome from February 18-21 that year, 1946 — is absorbed in prayer in the chapel of the city hall when the sound of the shots startles him. He grimaces and he gazes more intently now at the crucifix before which he is kneeling in prayer, his hands joined in supplication.

The door opens, and the seminarians who live in the building enter the chapel, in twos, dressed in white surplices over their black cassocks. They file into the church pews, typical narrow Polish pews with footboards at forty-five-degree angles, and recollect themselves in prayer while the shots slowly cease.

The Cardinal stands and turns to the clergymen.

"Is everyone here?" he demands severely.

"Karol Wojtyla is missing. He was in the march."

"Who gave him permission?"

"He is the vice president of the student union, a representative of the theology faculty. All the chairmen were at the head of the procession," explains the prefect.

"Let us pray for him. For everybody," the Cardinal concludes.

He turns to the altar and kneels.

Tadek and Wanda are caught in the raid. They are taken to the headquarters of the U.B., the terrible secret police, in the Square of Invalids, and they are separated.

Tadeusz is led down to the basement, which is already crammed with arrested students. The atmosphere is charged among these youth. They sing military and patriotic songs, sentimental and dirty ones, too. They chant slogans they learned at the march and yell obscene words. The soldiers keeping them in custody try to hide their sympathies. They sneak cigarettes to them and advise them to keep quiet. The officers of the U.B., on the other hand, are arrogant and derisive.

Every now and then the door opens. A policeman and two armed soldiers appear, read a list of names and lead these men to the interrogation.

Tadek is also called and brought to an office where an official with an anonymous voice is seated behind a desk. The arrested man is forced to sit on a stool beside him. The Polish eagle, missing its crown, hangs on the wall behind the official, along with a portrait of a sturdy Stalin in military outfit. A brawny warder stands behind Tadek, ready for a fight.

"Who did you receive your instructions from?" he is asked pointblank.

"The Holy Spirit."

The warder kicks the stool and Tadek lands on the floor. The official with slicked-back hair remains expressionless. Tadek gets up slowly, picks the stool up and sits down again.

"Where did you get the gun?"

"I didn't have a gun."

"The report (he points to a written document ont he desk) states that you had a nine-caliber pistol."

"It's not true."

"We have a witness."

"Yes, a crazy man or one who's having hallucinations."

Again the chair is kicked and Tadek tumbles. The warder stands the stool, upside down this time, and orders Tadek to sit on it. The official stops him, nodding.

"Not now. There's no time. Get him out."

Shoved into the hallway, Tadek bumps into Josef, who has grown a moustache. The young man wears a white shirt and red tie, indicating he is one of the U.B. Both men stop short, as if on instinct. But the shrewdness they learned in the woods, when they were partisans, comes into play. Neither one lets his astonishment show.

Josef is caught between wanting to help his old friend and wanting to show off his new power, his authority. He makes Tadek come to his office later that day. Josef appears in a double-breasted gtey jacket, grey shirt and dark tie. He speaks enthusiastically, in a superior tone.

"What did you get yourself into?"

"I got into this by accident, because of a girl. But why prohibit the celebration?"

"Should we celebrate a constitution that goes against the Soviet Union and venerates the Madonna Queen of Poland who is against us? Why should we denigrate ourselves?

"At least out of respect for tradition...."

"We will create new traditions," Josef states with conviction. "May 1st will take the place of May 3rd. The progressive tradition must defeat the reactionary one."

"The history of this country is a whole," argues Tadek. "You've assumed responsibility for it. But you can't choose the half you like, that suits you. After everything that happened today, you will be despised."

"We will transform that hate into obedience."

"Maybe, but only by terrorizing."

"We'll isolate the activists. Then the others will take our side because we can promise them peace and jobs. Obedience will become habit. Then we will wrap it in the cloak of patriotism. So they will believe in that, just like they believe in the Madonna now. That's right, my friend. We use our heads. We think. We don't sing litanies. Go home and think about it. You belong on our side, not with that herd."

And with those words, he points underground from where the notes of the hymn are issuing: "March, oh Poland, nation of great people, we will rest

60

from our labors in our houses..." Josef's disdain is obvious when he begins humming the melody to himself in mockery. Tadek remains seated, looking thoughtful. Then he continues:

"If you begin to split up, you will have to keep splitting endlessly. You'll have to divide us, breaking us up as a nation and a society. Even you will end up splitting apart, into ideological factions. In the end, we'll all lose our sense of identity. You're repeating exactly what our invaders have been doing to us for a hundred years. And for the same reasons as then — for law and order."

Josef is moved. He hesitates a moment before answering. Finally he says:

"Believe me, there's no choice, because the world is going to be divided. What kind of future can we have? It depends on who makes it. Come and work with us. We can't let it go to the dogs anymore. And now, go. You're free. Go home."

Tadek stands thinking for a few moments. He doesn't want to respond to Josef's final invitation yet. He only says:

"One more thing. There's a girl who was arrested, Wanda; they took her when they took me. Just do one more thing for me: get her out."

Josef reflects for a moment and then shakes his hand.

"Wait for her in the park outside here. And I'll be waiting for you. All right?"

Tadek shakes his hand thoughtfully, as if in agreement.

In the park near the branch of the U.B., Tadek waits on a bench, listening to the rustling of the birches. He keeps his eyes on the main door of the building, protected by barbed wire and guards. Suddenly Wanda comes out. Tadek runs toward her and sees she is crying hysterically.

"We did it! Why are you crying?"

Wanda pushes him away, her voice cracking.

"Get away from me. I don't want your help. I don't want your protection. I don't want to see you anymore. I belong down there, underground."

"But that's ridiculous."

"No, it's not. We have to fight back."

She bursts out crying again and grabs her chest, unable to express herself.

"To fight back for what?" Tadek demands angrily.

"For our hearts."

Tadek is shocked.

"What does heart mean in the language of the Rhapsodic Theater?"

"You'll never know that!"

The Metropolitan Archbishop of Cracow, Cardinal Adam Stefan Sapieha, has requested a meeting with the heads of the U.B. before the end of the day. The official in charge of the operation carried out against the students and his colleague Josef arrived late in the day. When they enter his office, they remain standing before the prelate, who also stands behind his desk, his fist resting on the top of the ink blotter.

In a hard, serious voice, he says:

"Let them go. Immediately. All of them. I am asking you. I am ordering you."

The man listens respectfully but seems unimpressed. Even Josef is indifferent, though he seems aware of the metropolitan's strong personality.

"If you do not, I will publish a Bishop's letter and have it read in all the churches. I will say that you have abolished a national and Catholic holiday, that you have violated an ancient tradition more than one hundred and fifty years old. And I will ask the whole world to help. If you won't respect our laws simply because we are less powerful than you are, you must at least respect our feelings because we are men like you. And anyway, I would imagine that the national unified government will uphold its good name."

"This government has an outstanding reputation," argues the official, "from the moment it was recognized by the western powers. But the world will certainly not take favorably to the news of those anti-semetic demonstrations in Cracow."

Josef is startled hearing these words. He gazes fixedly at his superior.

The Cardinal is indignant.

"It was not an anti-semitic demonstration!"

"But it could be interpreted as such," answers the man from the secret police, derisively.

"No," retorts Sapieha. "Even lies have their limits."

"But I say they don't," says the interlocutor in a falsely courteous tone. Then, turning to Josef:

"Isn't it true, comrade, that there were obvious signs of anti-semitism during the demonstration?"

"I don't know," he answers, growing pale.

"You yourselves said that you feared a *pogrom*."

"I certainly wasn't thinking of a *pogrom* of Jews."

"But it could have happened, and it still can." And addressing Josef, he adds, "So then, you'll have to change the public's opinion."

Then, turning to the Metropolitan Cardinal, he says in sudden agreement:

"I promise your Eminence that all of them will be freed tomorrow."

62

And taking his leave, he says partly for himself and partly for Josef:

"Let's say, almost all of them."

The Cardinal sits down and puts his head in his hands.

Shortly afterward, the vicar of the cathedral enters his office and approaches him on tiptoe. He says:

"Your Eminence, the boy's already back."

Shaking himself from his meditation, Sapieha answers:

"That's fine. Very fine. And tell me, when will he finish his studies?"

"Within a year, just a year."

"That's too long. He'll have to hurry it up. Do something so he's ready by the fall. By All Saints' Days. I want to ordain him myself. And then, on to Rome. Far from here. The next time it will be worse. It will get worse and worse."

THE PRIEST KAROL WOJTYLA

The young deacon lies prostrate on the floor of the chapel of the archbishoprie. He is dressed in white, the thick white silk cincture tight around his hips, closing around the borders of his deacon's stole. He lies on the floor like a willing victim. This is the most sublime of all the ritual gestures in the ordination of a priest. Cardinal Sapieha kneels before the faldstool which has been set on the base of the altar, donning his sumptuous embroidered robes of white silk which are for the feast of All Saints. The altar boys and other active participants in the ordination stand around him.

The chapel is aglow with festive lights, the altar is covered with flowers, all the seminarians from the class of theology have come to the celebration and are seated in the pews, now that Prince Sapieha's clandestine seminary has been able to return to its rightful headquarters on Podzamoze Street. Karol Wojtyla's closest friends look on, moved by the ceremony.

The singing of the Saints' litanies is over. The long, intimate and silent prayer of the newly ordained priest has been joined by the unanimous supplication of the congregation. He is now ready to stand and go before the Bishop who stands before him waiting solemnly, with the gold mitre on his head and the crosier in his hand, symbolizing his spiritual powers. Now strengthened in his purpose, he is ready to receive the sacrament of the ordination.

Sapieha places his hands to his head, and then all the other priests do likewise. Sapieha recites the ritual formula of ordination. Now Karol is a priest for eternity. He receives the episcopal insignia of the order. They spread the priestly chasable around his shoulders. The Bishop annoints his hands, hands him the chalice and paten, asks him to take the solemn oath of obedience and reverence to him and his successors, and kisses him on the cheeks, in the sign of peace. The gruff, severe Cardinal betrays no emotion. But after the ceremony, before dismissing him, he says, open-mindedly:

"Now, go out into the world, and don't be in a rush to come back. Observe. Learn. There will be a great deal to do. Much to save and repair. This requires a heart and a mind. Remember that — a heart and a mind."

These words show his obvious faith in Karol's seriousness.

The next day, Fr. Karol Wojtyla celebrates his first mass to commemorate All Dead Souls.

The Cathedral of Wawel is absorbed in the great ritual mass. The Archbishop is presiding over the rites, bedecked in black velvet robes embroidered in gold, and he is surrounded by all the ecclesiastical and lay dignitaries from Cracow's Catholic community, all of them dressed in elegant traditional costumes. A huge crowd has jammed into every corner of the cathedral to pray and join together in the singing of the ancient melodies of the Gregorian chants, which are incomparable in their evocation of the drama of pain, love and the certainty of everlasting life. Candles are everywhere, on the altar and in the chapels, illuminating the congregation gathered on this misty November morning.

A young priest dressed for mass, with the tricorn on his head and the veiled chalice in his hand, emerges from the sacristy. He is dressed in black, in accordance with the liturgy of the day, but his face radiates with joy, even in its composure. He walks alongside the congregation, preceded by two clergymen and accompanied by the bishop of the cathedral and by Marian, who has joined the priesthood, heading toward the spiral staircase that leads down to the crypt. This leads to the ancient Romanesque crypt of Saint Leonard, where a small crowd of friends is already waiting. His colleagues from the Rhapsodic Theater are there, among them the "professor," and the best of his old friends from the Solvay plant, including the worker who picked up his bloody briefcase, and finally those whose friendship had helped him during difficult years of the war. Beneath the lamps shaped like the royal crown, the names Sobieski, Kosciuszko, Poniatowski, Wisniowiecki appear ont he tombs. This is the distant but glorious past of *Poland semper fidelis.*

But a less distant past also lives int he heart of the new priest, and this is what he intends to bring before God during his first celebration of the Eucharist: it is the memory of his dead family, his mother, father and brother, and also of the thousands and millions of Poles sacrified to the Moloch* of war and persecution.

He walks up to the stone altar in the apse where the flames of two lit tapers are flickering. He makes the sign of the cross and delivers the first words of the mass:

"Introibo ad altare Dei."

"Ad Deum qui laetificat juventuten meam," the congregation responds in chorus.

When the young priest says, "I will go before the altar of God, God who filled my youth with joy," such a long pause follows these meaningful words that the vicar of the cathedral, becoming unnerved, nearly prompts him.

Tadeusz has also come for the moving rite. But his spirit is elsewhere. He is next to Wanda, who sits in the front row, out of his reach, intensely following the prayers of the new priest.

Karol spends several weeks in Wadowice, his native town, where he still has many old friends. This is where he will celebrate many of his first masses and begin his priestly duties, the work of watching over souls, which he knows is his rightful calling.

Then, obeying the wishes of his Bishop, he goes directly to Rome, where he attends the Pontifical University of Saint Thomas Aquinas and lives with the Dominican Fathers. Within two years he is ready to receive his doctorate with his thesis on *The Concept of Faith in Saint John of The Cross,* and the academic title is also approved by the Jagellonica University in Cracow. In the meantime, he has come to know Rome intimately in all its aspects — ancient and contemporary, civil and papal. In 1947, he spends his vacation in France and Belgium to study the actual pastoral experience there, in a society undergoing rapid transformation, as that one was, immediately after the war.

Returning to Poland in 1948, he becomes vice parish priest in the country town of Niegowic for a year, and then spends two years in Cracow in the

---

* A deity whose worship was marked by the burning of children given by their own parents.

parish of Saint Florian. He loves the apostolate, particularly the young, the students, the ailing. His confessional is always full of people. Since he had started to make periodic trips to the mountains and lakes, he had been able to deepen his developing relationship with the youth. The young people call him "uncle" and have a faith and respect for him that is normally reserved for an old, learned teacher. Following the wishes of Cardinal Sapieha, he prepares a thesis which will permit him to teach at the university level, examining the philosophy of Max Scheler. In 1958 he receives the teacher's degree from the Faculty of Theology of Jagellonica University in Cracow, submitting a thesis *On the Possibility of Creating a Catholic Ethic Founded on the Philosophical System of Max Scheler.* But he doesn't get bogged down in philosophy. He writes long poems, short verses and dramatic works. He contributes to the healthy lives of Polish youth. He submits himself to the exhaustion of long trips and camping expeditions. He teaches life by conversing and living. And most of all, he prays.

On July 23, 1951, Cardinal Sapieha dies and is universally mourned. Wojtyla never dreamed that he would be chosen to succeed him as Archbishop. For twelve years the diocese has been provisionally entrusted to the aged Archbishop from Leopoli, Monsignor Eugene Baziak. In 1953 Karol Wojtyla is named professor of social ethics at the Cracow Seminary. In 1954 he is also invited by the Catholic University in Lublino to offer a standard course. These are two commitments to which he dedicates himself with great straightforwardness and vigor, proving himself to be a true teacher of a whole generation of priests and students.

On July 4, 1958, he is elected auxiliary Bishop for Monsignor Baziak in the diocese of Cracow. He is thirtyeight years old, the youngest Polish Bishop. He is ordained as Bishop in Wawel on September 28 of that year.

When Monsignor Baziak dies on February 14, 1962, Bishop Wojtyla is chosen to run the archdiocese as the city vicar. The solemn celebration when he takes possession of the cathedral in Wawel takes place March 8. The Pope names him a Cardinal on June 26, 1967.

He remains a professor in Lublino, he remains the "uncle" of his young friends, all the while building an intense ministry as Bishop, amid all sorts of problems created by Poland's political situation, which causes many obstacles for the church. Meanwhile Rome is taking notice of him. He is one of the main participants in the Second Vatican Council, of subsequent Bishops' synods, and of various cultural and religious events and meetings around the world. In 1966, he celebrates the anniversary of the first millennium of the Christening of Poland, along with the Primate Cardinal Stefan Wyszynski and all the nation's Bishops, and its faithful people.

68

Nowa Huta

In the late 1940s, rapid political and economic changes take place. The nation's politics undergo an extraordinary dismal period that lasts until 1956, three years after Stalin's death. The relationship between the state and the church is equally difficult. Bishops Baraniak and Kaczmarek are arrested, priests and religious figures are tried, the Primate Cardinal is confined to his quarters (compulsory residence), forbidden to have any contact with his parishoners. Only the economy seems to move toward a period of great expansion. Communist leaders decide to build an enormous steel complex near Cracow, and alongside it a model socialist city, without God or church, to be called Nowa Huta.

At the construction sites of the worker metropolis that is being built, amid mud, overturned earth and chugging bulldozers, barracks go up which will accommodate the thousands of workers engaged in the labor, and men arrive from all over the country. Wladek is among those who have decided to take up new and perhaps profitable work and he has left behind his farmhouse in Kalwaria.

An employee seated at a table processes information on the new workers. A squabble breaks out, provoking comments and protests from those workers who are waiting their turns. One of them, Wladek, in fact, demands the right to bring his mother, wife and son with him right away. This had been promised him, and so it should be. The employee explains that the houses must be built before they can be occupied. But Wladek feels that he was taken advantage of and demands at least a written guarantee. The employee, cajoling him a little, scolding him a little, explains that this request is utterly out of the question. They'll discuss it again at a later date. But in spite of the uproar behind him, Wladek refuses to budge until the employee guarantees him, at least with a handshake, that there will be a place for his family to live, which the employee finally does, although without conviction.

After many months the houses are constructed and Wladek is assigned an apartment. Wladek and his wife drag a dresser up several flights of stairs in the huge project building that has just been whitewashed and is still wet with lime. Their son, Staszek, is with them, hauling a basket full of pots, and his old grandmother, who is clutching a sacred image. It is an animated scene, for it is not easy to carry a dresser up a stairway. The conversation between husband and wife, a bit breathless and cross, is full of joking. When they finally reach their new lodging, Staszek is struck by the missing fireplace.

"How will we cook?"

"There's a gas stove. Don't you see it?"

The boy goes up to the burners, turns the knobs, does the same with the faucets and light switches.

But the old mother can only think of one thing.

"Wladek, put a hook up for me there, in the middle of the wall."

"But why make a hole in a new wall?"

"Just do it," says Wladek's wife.

It is difficult to make the nail stay in. The plaster crumbles and pieces shower down to the floor. But finally it is done. The old woman hangs her painting up. It shows a large, darkened image of the Madonna of Kalwaria Zebrzydowska. They realize now how small and low-ceilinged the apartment really is in comparison to the humble but airy farmhouse they've left behind. The two women kneel immediately, and Wladek's mother begins to recite the prayer *Angelus Domini* aloud. Glancing at his father and then at the two women, Staszek finally kneels, too. But the door has been left ajar, as was always done in Kalwaria. And the other tenants on their floor come and peer in, curious about what is going on inside the room: two women and a young boy on their knees, praying. Wladek, embarrassed and irritated by the situation, slams the door.

70

THE DREAMS AND DISAPPOINTMENTS OF THE '50s

At the building sites in Nowa Huta the house is all the news. The construction of the city and the work complex is in progress, and there are placards all around with slogans, dates, figures and blueprints of the work planned, as well as rules of behavior for the establishment of a socialist society.

The optimism of the publicity stands in contrast, however, to the topsy-turvy landscape where the old demolished houses lie in ruins, where mud reigns supreme and where barracks are still the main accommodation for the workers.

It also stands in contrast to the listless, miserable crowds of people who are frequently forced to march in endless files under the portraits of Stalin and Bierut, under the caricatures of obese capitalists and ridiculous-looking priests, and order the omnipresent doves of peace.

A group of young men associated with the *Sluzba Polsce* (Polish Service) advances in green uniforms, singing a nursery rhyme as if it were a hymn: "We of the ZMP, we of the ZMP, we don't fear other side." The ZMP is the union of Polish youth, organized by the powers that be.

Tadeusz has the impression of seeing the old Baudienst, come to life again in the new Poland. He tries to dismiss this unpleasant thought from his

71

mind and to concentrate on the leather bag resting on his knees. He arrives at Nowa Huta in a black automobile, sitting by himself in one corner of the back seat, accompanied by the driver and an active member of the Communist Party. Tadeusz has become somebody. He's written a book on the new city in construction. He's even won a political literary prize. The party is sending him to Nowa Huta to meet face to face the participants of this new social reality.

Oblivious to the disorder outside the limosine, the activist turns to Tadeusz and says enthusiastically:

"We're transforming the landscape. Civilization is conquering nature. The people are growing up, coming of age. This is the struggle of the new against the old, comrade!, and I must say that literature is helping us along."

"But will anyone come to this meeting?" asks Tadeusz, growing nervous.

"Let me handle it. You hear that? The announcement is being made throughout the area," answers the activist.

He opens the car window so he can hear the voice on the loudspeaker more clearly:

"Comrades, you are all invited to meet an eminent writer, winner of the national prize, author of the book about the construction of our foundries..."

Tadeusz feels calmer now. He fixes the knot of his red tie on his white shirt, straightens his cap, squeezes the bag with the copy of his first book.

He's led into a barracks which has been transformed into a meeting hall. The walls are decorated with portraits, banners and slogans. There is a row of benches, all of them empty.

"There's nobody here," says Tadek.

"Don't worry," responds the activist.

The young men from the **ZMP** file into the room in step, singing, "... we don't fear the other side." Shoving and yelling, they take their seats in a flurry. Putting their muddy feat up on the benches in front of them, practically on the backs of their comrades.

"Shall we begin?" Tadeusz asks hesitantly.

"The people from the administration aren't here yet!" The activist moves around with the confidence of an experienced director. In fact, several minutes later, several people in civilian dress slip in, men and women employed by the state's office of finances and expenditures. They file into the first vacant rows timidly and sit down, seemingly annoyed at whoever subjected them to such an unpleasant duty.

When Tadek notices Wanda among them, he steps off the stage, surprised and pleased, and clasps her hand. Wanda looks back at him without

72

surprise or affection. She looks worn out, withered. She answers his questions apathetically, perhaps out of prudence.

"I work here. I'm a typist."

"What about the theater?"

"It was closed down. Your friend Josef took care of that. We were advised of the party's opinion—a "parasite theater" because we had a romantic repertory instead of presenting political propaganda, as instructed.

Actually, the actors had been forced to disband after the resignation of Mieczyslaw Kotlarczyc, the "professor" who'd been directing them. He had been forced to quit despite the fact that his actions during the occupation were worthy of praise. The actors were only allowed to accept parts in repertories approved by the state. Because Wanda had protested and expressed solidarity, she'd been forbidden to work on any stage.

Wanda looks for a seat, but Tadeusz pushes her for more news:
"And Marian?"

"He's in isolation, so to speak."

"We have to talk later," Tadeusz says under his breath.

"Will this last long? Because it's hard to get back to the city much later."

"So why are you staying if you're in such a rush?" Tadek snaps, offended.

"To be honest, I'm forced to." Wanda has taken on the same ironic tone she once had.

Everyone is seated. The activist breaks the ice.

"Comrades, friends, today we have the honor of having a young, eminent writer with us." Polite applause fills the room, and Tadek responds with a bow, getting to his feet, then sitting again. After a brief embarrassing silence, he begins speaking:

"It's already late, almost evening, and you're all here after a long day of work."

"But we'll listen gladly," says the activist flatteringly.

"To tell the truth, I would like to look and listen. I came here to learn. Has anybody already read my book? Would anybody like to ask a question?"

When the activist nods, a young boy from the organization stands, produces a sheet of paper and reads some cliches about socialist literature distractedly.

"No," snaps Tadeusz. "If that's all we have to say to one another, it's not worth it. Let's go home. It's better."

"Comrade," the activist calls to him.

"I've written a book about the birth of Nowa Huta. I came here to find out from you if what I wrote is correct. Maybe it's not. You have to tell me. That's the only reason for talking—to confide the truth to each other, the whole truth."

Wanda, who was intently studying the tips of her shoes until then, raises her head and stares at him. Tadek notices her attention and continues with intensity, for her.

"There must be a connection between us. A lasting, solid connection. If there isn't, it's not worthwhile."

The people in the room just sit, looking unreachable, unimpressed.

There's a lot of silence. Perplexed, the activist rises:

"Does anyone have any questions? No? Perhaps it really is too late—."

The young men get up noisily and rush for the door. Even the employees head swiftly toward the exit, albeit more gracefully.

"Comrade, this is not a good thing," the activist says to Tadek, indignantly.

Tadek sidesteps and follows the fleeing audience to find Wanda. But she's already gone, swallowed up by the darkness. Instead, he comes upon a boy in the ZMP uniform. It's Staszek, Wladek's son. He asks Tadek point blank:

"Excuse me, sir, does God exist?"

"Why are you asking me?"

"The people in command. Of course, if there's no God, then we're beasts that should be led. But if there is one, then we have something inside of us that cannot be seen, that they don't want to see. Tell me whether or not he exists. Are they right or not?"

"I don't know."

At this the boy lowers his voice and says impertinently:

"Then what do you write about?"

"Precisely about that. Not knowing?"

"But I can reach that conclusion, too. Excuse me." He turns and vanishes into the darkness.

Father Marian, who has been held in prison for some time already during the severe repression of the church, is brought to the offices of the secret police for an interrogation. He is drawn, his clothes are ragged, his shoes have no laces. He sits on a stool, under the intense spotlight and repeats mechanically:

"It's not true. I don't belong to any anti-Communist organization. I have never done anything against the state."

Sitting behind the desk is the same official who spoke with Sapieha on the evening of May 3, 1946. He is listening to the prisoner with a look of boredom and scorn, while the secretary, seated at the typewriter, records the proceedings. Now it's time for the meeting to take another turn. The man sends away the clerk, turns off the spotlights, draws up to Marian with a kindly air and begins a strange conversation:

"Let's talk man to man now. Would you like some tea? A cigarette? It's allowed here. The Bishop won't see you."

Marin refuses but immediately feels relieved and a bit more comfortable on the hard stool. The official pauses, lights a cigarette, paces, then comes back, persuasively adding:

"Look, father, whether or not you confess, there will be a trial in any case. It would be better if you confessed. You would certainly suffer less."

"But I can't confess to that which I didn't do."

"If we want to, we can bring forth the evidence in any case. Because, father, there are no innocent men. On the other hand, if we find we don't want to, we will not find the evidence and we'll let you go." He pauses. "Have you ever heard of patriotic priests?"

"No."

"I see. News of this sort doesn't reach prison. It's a truly noble movement. There are many people in it much like yourself—dedicated, energetic, modern. They understand the times. They don't want the church to linger in the battles of the past. If you would meet them, if you would like to influence people in that way—for example, young seminary students. You could assume a very important role in the new church."

Marian says nothing. His long pause qualifies his answer:

"I'm a priest."

"That's just it," insists the other.

"To be a priest means to be faithful."

"Of course, to the real religious mission."

"To the church!"

"Yes, naturally to the church. Our state allows freedom of worship."

"Wherever the Bishop is, that's where the church is!"

"The Bishop? He's a weak man. He can make mistakes. The church is a community of people who want to enjoy peace and progress."

"Each and every Bishop, along with the Pope, carries out the teachings of the church, which are infallible beaucase they come from—."

"That's enough," the official says, cutting him off. "Go back to your cell and reflect on your future. It's entirely in our hands."

Marian smiles feebly.

"Certainly *not* in yours. In God's."

"First a girl and now a priest! What are you up to?" Josef, sitting at the desk in his office, surrounded by symbols of the regime and signs of discreet success, replies to Tadek, who has come to the headquartes of the secret police to intercede for the release of Marian.

"He's your brother, you ought to understand me!" explains Tadek.

"I understand... And... does he have many other relatives?" comments Josef ironically.

"Jozek! It's a trifle for you. Besides, he hans't done anything bad. They seized him to put fear into the others."

"I have my doubts about that. You never know. And then, in the party nothing is a trifle."

"Not as a rule," Takek objects, "but this is an exception!"

"In the party there are no exceptions!"

Confronted with Jozek's hardness, Tadek realizes for the first time that he is dealing with someone unknown, different from the man he saved and brought to the partisans years before. He has changed; he has become a stranger. Nevertheless, Tadek tries one more time.

"Won't you do it for me?"

"I am thinking of you especially," is Jozek's answer. Then, looking around him, as if he is trying to overcome his annoyance, he indicates the glass door and suggests: "Shall we go out on the terrace? You can't even breathe in here."

From the height of the terrace they can see the cheering panorama of the city spread out before them. A light wind stirs around them. Jozek seems less tense without the face of Stalin over his shoulder. In a different voice he begins to talk to his old friend.

"You saved my life once. And now I want to save yours."

"My life!" Tadek is stupefied.

"Yes, yours. You must realize that to step outside of this system is to die. And don't ask me why. Because it was set up this way and neither you nor I were around at the time."

"But now we are," Tadek objects.

"Now! Now the balls roll as they were thrown; if they bump, if they col-

76

lide, they rebound. The game is dictated by an uncontrollable power and it cannot be stopped. They can only watch the movements and wait for the outcome. Will you let me make a prophecy? We are all destined to burn in the crematorium of politics. Many have already gone in—opponents tied to the old regime, the officers of the old guard, the underground, the landowners and the peasants. Now it is the priests' turn. Tomorrow it will be the turn of the writers and artists. When it is over, there will be only a handful of ashes left."

"But what's the purpose of all this," Tadek asks, horrified.

Jozek leans forward, rests his forearms on the railing and looks down into the void. Seriously he continues:

"I was asking myself that question over and over when you found me under the table in the old ghetto. What is the purpose of all this killing? You said to me, 'Rise and come.' Now I say to you, 'Rise and come!' I say to you, 'Save yourself!'"

"No, you are only trying to persuade me that I should leave someone helpless who is in great need."

"Forget about it. I warn you that there are certain things you should not ask of me and I should not do, or even hear about."

"But Jozek, what has happened to you?" he says with agitation, taking him by the arms.

"What has happened to me? It's merely that I have realized that I cannot evade making a choice: liberty or life."

"But what is life worth without liberty?"

"Worth! The accomplishment of the great principles, the great laws! Of the law of progress! Of the dialectic! The great story of civilization, of the generations, of the nations is made up of many letters. Every single human existence is one of those letters and goes to make up an immense book."

"If that is true, it is not worthwhile worrying so much about individual lives—yours, mine. From what are you trying to protect yourself and me?"

"From an accidental, senseless, antihistorical annihilation. You are a writer and you are running the risk of becoming no one. Do you understand? No one! A man without a name, because we gave you the name. And we can take it away!"

"And if you are wrong? And if your great enius Josef Stalin is wrong, too? If the true cause of all things should be in another sphere altogether? Perhaps, out of the whole history of humanity, what really counts is only what counts to me now."

"And what might that be?"

"Listen, Jozek! Marian has been a true friend to me. He ended up at Auschwitz because of me. On top of that, I love his sister. I really love her. I am ready to sacrifice everything to save him, even my literary career and my name. Forget about your dialectic. Make a telephone call on his behalf. I know that a telephone call from you is more than sufficient. Will you do it? Will you take a risk for me, as I took a risk for you? Will you do it or will you let me down?"

Tadek has spoken with passion; he has played his last card in making this plea. Jozek looks him in the eye for a long time. Then he looks at his watch.

"Excuse me, I have a meeting."

While Tadek walks down the steps of the secret police headquarters, Josef seats himself again behind his desk. He thinks and stays a long time without moving, as if gripped by an internal struggle. Then he lifts the phone off the hook and slowly dials one number, and another and another, speaks firmly for several minutes, hangs up and goes out.

TENSIONS IN THE NEW SOCIETY

Tadek has an anger burning inside him that will not leave him in peace. His last talk with Jozek has unleashed contradictory feelings in him: rebellion, remorse, selfcritical evaluations, a desire to vindicate himself. He spends the days in his room full of books, seated at his typewriter, now in meditation, now tapping out nervously on the sheets of paper things he would never publish. There is a knock on the door and a message. The color goes out of his face. It is a note from his father telling him that his mother is gravely ill. Some time ago, when he had made a name for himself as a writer, he had left home. It seemed to him that it shrunk him to be around his parents, who were frozen in their outmoded ideas about people and things, views that no longer coincided with his own. But the heavy news shakes him. He is assailed by a sense of guilt. He had abandoned them just at their time of greatest need—material need possibly and emotional need certainly.

He grabs a light overcoat off the wall, throws it over his shoulders and hastens to his parents' house.

His father, even more bent and feeble, shows in his face the signs of the accumulated fatigue of taking care of his sick wife for so long. He sees his son and shows no surprise. He greets him as if he had been there all along.

He accompanies him to the sickroom, which is permeated by the smell of medication. In the big bed, his mother is propped on the pillows, breathing with difficulty, and lies back as if she has exhausted her strenght. Hearing someone enter, she raises her eyelids slightly and almost ceases breathing. Her husband bends over her and murmurs to her that Tadeusz—Tadzius, as she called him when he was a baby—has come.

She closes her eyes again, recommences her labored breathing as if disappointed. Her husband, who knows her well, understands. He caresses her head and says:

"The priest who is bringing you Jesus will be here soon."

At the frontiers of life, when each person is alone face to face with the mystery, all the real values in which one believes rise to the surface of consciousness, among them, as time and energy are increasingly restricted, those that one feels to be the most important.

Tadek is not able to understand this desire of his mother, so clear, on the other hand, to her, even in her state of semi-consciousness, and he says to his father:

"She has lost consciousness!"

"She is wandering," he says, as if he wanted to defend her. Meanwhile he wipes her brow, moistens her lips.

"Has she ever asked about me?"

"Yes, certainly."

His father asks Tadeusz to leave him alone for a moment to change the invalid, who is covered with sweat. The son goes out into the little living room where everything speaks of the far-away years of his childhood. But he also sees signs of his recent success: a copy of the books with the emphatic titles *Epic of Nowa Huta* and *The Dignity of Human Speech*, distributed in huge editions, even translated into Russian and Czech; newspaper clippings with his photographs at official ceremonies or prize-giving occasions; a recent newspaper with the text of one of his speeches. He picks it up with a sense of revulsion. He crushes the newspaper into a ball and throws it away.

The doorbell rings softly. Tadeusz goes to open the door and finds the priest with the sacraments. He is a tall, robust man in his thirties with a slight, deliberate stoop. His clear, deep voice gives the Christian words of greeting, "Let Jesus Christ be praised." That face, which he knows, strikes him and disturbs him now with its extraordinary maturity. He is especially moved by those eyes—deep, kind and very alive. With an embarassed gesture, Tadek motions for him to come in. The priest quickly and in silence takes off his black overcoat. Underneath are the white surplice and stole over the long vestment, and suspended from the neck on a thin silk cord is a small burse of white silk with the letters IHS embroidered in gold.

The priest is Karol Woityla, assistant parish priest of Saint Florian, and in the little burse he carries the Eucharist.

The father comes to greet him, kneels on both knees before him for the sake of Him he carries, and brings him into the sickroom.

"Let us go out. He will confess her now."

"But she is unconscious!" Tadeusz says.

"Her heart is alive. Father Karol knows it well and knows how to talk to her."

Tadek, disturbed because he is so much outside of these proceedings, exasperated by his father's long silences, which sound to his conscience like a reproof, whereas they are actually just a mark of courtesy and respect, remarks sceptically, "Her heart! A muscle now torn to shreds—."

He trails off. His father remains standing, bows his head, folds his hands and prays. Tadeusz plays nervously with the buttons on his jacket.

The door opens and the priest makes a sign that they can enter. The father enters; Tadek stays at the threshold. On the little table by the bed the two candles flanking the Crucifix are lit. Father Karol recites in Latin the prayers for the communion of the sick; he gives the woman a small piece of the consecrated host, pours a glass of water to help her swallow it and remains attentively at her side, softly stroking her hair.

Tadek goes away from the door, stands facing the window and mechanically watches the traffic going by in the street; he does not notice when his mother dies.

Only when the priest comes out does he have a leap of conscience and asks, "Is she dead?"

"May God comfort her, my brother."

"But I do not cry."

"May God grant you the gift of tears. It is very fortunate that you were near your mother at that moment."

"But I wasn't at my mother's side. Just you and my father. What do you mean it was fortunate?"

"Fortunate for you. The memory of this death will remain with you forever, it will grow and you will reap the fruits of it."

"What on earth do you mean?"

"I know what I am talking about. I was far away when my dear ones died and I know how much I lost. Therefore I know how much you have been enriched. Goodbye till we meet again."

Tadek approaches the big office in the heart of Cracow where several hundred typists serve "the builders of the new social order." He has nothing in his hand: no purse, no book, no file. He acts bewildered and unsure. He looks around, screws up his courage, opens the door. The clicking of the typewriters assails him with increased intensity. The women nearest to him raise their heads incuriously, stop typing, look at him. The noise grows fainter. Then Wanda, too, raises her head. She looks at Tadek, who succeeds in locating her in a distant row and makes a sign to her. I? she seems to ask incredulously. He nods yes. She rises, walks over to him and goes out with him into the corridor.

"Why did you come here?"

"I had to talk to you."

"Well, here I am."

"I have been looking for you since yesterday. I didn't know you worked here."

"At present I am prohibited from working in the theater. Perhaps you have something urgent you want me to type?"

"Don't make fun of me. I came for another reason."

"I'm listening."

There is a lot of movement in the corridor.

"Perhaps not here," he says.

Wanda agrees to go out to the street. But she has no coat on and shivers with cold. To break the silence she says, "Thank you for Marian. They released him yesterday."

"I didn't come to be thanked. I wanted to see you. I need you."

"I heard that there was some trouble about the new book, that you are no longer in favor. It must be disappointing..."

"That's not important now."

Even the banality of the conversation betrays a new state of affairs. Wanda for the first time looks at this man with new eyes. She realizes that something is happening to her where he is concerned. Or perhaps she only now has the courage to admit it. Tadek says, "My mother is dead. I am realizing how much I loved her. And I have no one I can say this to. I thought that—but perhaps I was mistaken. Please excuse me, I'm so sorry."

He turns and walks away quickly. Wanda follows him with her eyes and just as he is about to disappear among the other passersby, she realizes that she wants him to stay. She calls, "Tadek." He hears her, stops, turns. They run into each other's arms.

It is a warm spring day. Tadek goes into the Church of Saint Florian in the Kleparz quarter of Cracow. He pretends to be a visitor, in order not to attract the attention of the handful of faithful entering and leaving. But when he goes by the second confessional on the left, in which a little red light is on to show that assistant parish priest Karol Woityla is in attendance, with a rapid movement he ducks in and kneels. The light goes out.

"Father, I haven't..."

"Let Jesus Christ be praised."

"Father, I haven't come to confess myself, but to comply with a formality."

"Which formality?"

"I want to be married in church. And I have to swear that I have confessed myself."

"It isn't a formality. It's a sacrament."

"But I am not a believer. I am only doing it for my fiance, who..."

"What do you not believe in?"

Tadek is surprised and even embarrassed by the question. He answers, "If we must talk, let us come out of here. I do not feel at my ease."

"But if we are to comply with this 'formality,' one of us must be seated and the other kneeling," the priest says in a firm tone.

Then Tadek, who has thought about it at length in advance, pronounces his act of non-faith. And the priest with patience and astuteness enters into a dialogue with him, showing him the contradictions in his reasoning without offending, and yet salvaging all the positive aspects in order to show him how close he is to that faith he believes he must deny.

"I do not believe that God revealed himself, descending to earth and leaving his teaching," is Tadek's first sally.

To this the priest calmly asks an original question: "All right. But tell me what you do believe."

"I belive in the capacity of man to raise himself above his own nature and to give life to new modes of existence."

"And if I were to tell you that that is the same thing as what you said you do not believe?"

"But how?" objects Tadeusz in surprise. "Either God created us and descended to us, or we created Him and are raising ourselves to his level. There is no alternative to this dilemma."

"God created us in his image and likeness. And we made Him in the likeness of what?"

"Of ourselves."

"In our likeness we have historically created tyrants, dictators and puffed-up clowns. But when we think of God, we imagine him to be holy, disinterested, full of love. He is something more than our own likeness. In any case, what criteria do you use in examining these grave problems?"

"The criteria of pure reason, which distinguishes true from false, good from evil, what is perfect from what is corrupt."

"But when you speak of pure reason," interjects the priest, "you are only one logical step from the act of faith. Reason is a good we receive, not one that comes out of ourselves. How can we have what we have not received? Have patience..."

"But I don't want to have patience. Nor do I feel that I am wrong. I just want to be free. If I wanted to submit, I would submit today, to be in peace."

"Not all the faith and all the submission in the world can insure peace."

"I was talking about inner peace. I know that if right now I were to confess my sins and receive absolution, I would feel tranquil. But I have no intention of doing it."

"You are refusing a medicine, even knowing you need it and it would do you good."

"I am refusing a drug. I want to be free, conscious and responsible through and through."

"You are drugging yourself with an illusion of liberty."

It is here that the dialogue reaches the crucial point. Tadek is imbued with Marxist doctrine; he admits it and declares it. He cannot think of an argument to counter what the priest has said. Instead, he responds with a question.

"So you also talk about the illusions of liberty?"

"Why, who else talks about them?"

"The Marxists."

"Marxism defines the limits of freedom referring back to the inviolable laws of history. Christ, on the other hand, refers to the laws of the heart. He affirms straight out that the only slavery worthy of a man is that of the heart."

"Slavery of the hearth? And what might that be?" objects Tadek, in a tone almost indulgent.

"You want to get married and you don't know? You are a writer and you don't know?"

"How do you know I am a writer?"

"I know," answers the priest, a little embarrassed.

And Tadek replies coldly, "Let's not talk about personal things. Here is

84

the form from the parish office that is supposed to attest to my confession. Do you want to sign it?''

''Certainly,'' is the answer. And then, stressing the words, ''Just let me add one thought, and it is this, that 'heart' in the language of theology signifies 'person,' and 'person' in the language of ethics signifies 'God.' If you are capable of loving someone, you are closer to God than you think. Where is the form?''

Tadek rises with the form in his hand. He stands in front of the confessional. The two windows open slightly, but without revealing the face of the person inside. A breviary is extended on which the form is supported. A robust hand fills in the spaces of the ''formality'' with a ballpoint pen.

1950: A winter evening at Nowa Huta. The construction of the satellite city at the gates of Cracow has passed a few more milestones. One can already get an idea of the future streets and squares laid out according to an ambitious plan. But here are still no pavements or sidewalks, and the people continue to labor their way through the mud.

Wladek's mother, old and bent, wrapped in an old peasant shawl, walks into the wind, giving her hand to Staszek, her grandson who is now twelve. In the other hand she carries a candle, like all the others who are converging from different parts of the housing under construction and all heading in the same direction.

They all go into a shed distinguished on the outside by a small cross of lighted lamps. They shake the snow off themselves, try to warm up a bit. At the back of the shed, in a tiny space that serves as a sacristy, Marian puts on the sacred vestments to say the mass. Suddenly the light goes out. There is a slight turmoil in the shed because of the unexpected occurrence. Marian searches in vain for matches to light a candle when suddenly a lantern shines in his face.

''Reverend father, you must leave this place immediately.''

It is an official and a policeman, who have first cut the wires for the lights and now are delivering the eviction order.

''But I have a permit from the town council to hold religious meetings.''

''Yes, but the shed is scheduled for demolition.''

''Then give us another building in its place.''

''We are not obligated to do that.''

''But the Constitution guarantees freedom of worship.''

''There are enough churches in Cracow.''

"No, not enough. Besides, these people live here, work here. They have the right to have their own church."

"You can discuss that with the authorities. We have our orders and we have to follow them."

The official examines the walls of the tiny sacristy in the light of the lamp. He sees the main light switches.

"This wiring is dangerous. A fire could break out at any time."

"No danger of that anymore, since you cut the wires..."

"Tell the people to go. It is against the law to meet in the dark."

"There's no lack of light here!"

He opens the door of the sacristy. The chapel is illuminated by dozens of candles. In the light of their flames the faces of the faithful watching the sacristy intently appear so strong, composed and severe that the official hesitates and withdraws, saying, "All right, go ahead tonight, since the people are already here. But tomorrow..."

"Tomorrow we will go and ask..." Marian starts to say.

The policeman points skyward with his thumb.

"You're right. Up there."

The congregation starts to sing "In the Silence of the Night."

A Kind of Thaw

In March of 1953 the Soviet dictator Josef Stalin died. A general unrest mushroomed in the countries under the influence of the Soviet Union. This unrest was heightened after the historic "report" that the foreign minister of the USSR, Nikita Khrushchev, read in February of 1956 before the general assembly of the Communist Party's Twentieth Congress, it marked the toppling of a myth, with public acknowledgment of Stalin's crimes and errors.

In June of that year, in Poland, there was the revolt of Poznan. The Cegielski factories went on strike against low wages and police repression. Clashes with the law enforcement agents left about seventy people dead on the field and one hundred people injured. The Communist chief Gomulka was released from prison and in October he assumed the office of Secretary of the Central Committee of the Party. In October authorities also released the Cardinal Primate Wyszynski. While Hungary was burning in its heroic and unavailing revolt, Poland was saved, thanks to the renewed leadership of the party and to the church's mediating support. In 1956, Cardinal Wyszynski exorted the faithful to remain calm and in 1957 he urged them not to desert the polls at the general elections, for the greater good of the country. From that vote, eleven Catholic deputies of the Znak group came to take part in the parliament, up to then completely controlled by the Communists. In addition, the movement of Catholic intellectuals was born and began its activity. It would have great impact on the succession of events in the years ahead.

It is a day in autumn, around early evening. There is a drizzle. On an empty road in an old neighborhood of Cracow, a man walks slowly. The collar of his coat is raised, his head bent, his hands in his pockets. No one recognizes him as the toplofty official of the secret police, who had once been, up to a short time before, the former resistance fighter Josef, nicknamed Jozek. He stops as he approaches the apartment building where Tadek lives. He looks up at the windows of his apartment, hesitates, takes a few steps toward the entrance but changes his mind and continues on with his slow walk. Unexpectedly, Tadek comes out of the house and hurriedly proceeds in the same direction as Jozek. He reaches him and passes by, without recognizing the man. But Jozek realizes who he is. He summons the courage to call out:

"Tadek!"

"Jozek! What are you doing here?"

"Just going out for a stroll. No special reason."

"No special reason?"

Jozek gives a shrug and attempts a feeble smile.

"I was tempted to stop by to see you. I never came to pay you a visit..."

"After the war, in 1945, I invited you to stay with me, but you didn't want to. If you want to pay me a visit now, come on up. Wanda's there. I'm going to the drugstore for a minute and I'll be right back."

"No, I''ll go with you. So you got married! To that girl in the theater?"

"That's the one."

"And are you happy? The last time you came to me on account of her brother. I did what I could to help him, you know?"

Tadek stares at him quizzically. What did he mean? Jozek understands the look.

"No, I'm not looking for an alibi. I don't need any excuse for my new position. On the other hand—."

"That time you struck me as being really cruel. I decided that I'd never have anything to do with you again."

They walk in silence. Then Jozek stops all of a sudden.

"I really took Stalin seriously!"

"Was that possible? Didn't you know anything?"

"I knew a whole lot, just about everything, but I thought it was neces-

88

sary... maybe the ghetto, maybe the extermination that was going on, they made me begin to doubt the man and rely on the movements of history..."

"And now?"

"I turned in my card to the party. I'm no longer anybody."

They reach the drugstore. They stop for a moment. Tadek is touched by this inner drama. He simply asks:

"What are you going to do?"

Jozek starts in, he tries to display some selfassurance, even though his state of perplexity and doubt show through his whole person.

"I'm going to take a new look at history. I'd like to—perhaps—write something on the history of the Jews in Poland."

Tadek clasps his hand.

"Drop by and see us some time!"

"Maybe one day," says Jozek.

On the other front, things are going decidedly better. Wanda walks along Starowislana Road, today named after the heroes of Stalingrad. She is happy, humming and smiling to herself, completely immersed in her thoughts. She crosses the entrance leading to a courtyard, and comes upon her old friends of the theater, of the happy theater days, who have a date to meet her there. Excited and jovial, they greet each other noisily, as though they haven't met for a long time. A little later, the "professor" joins them. He is serious and reserved as always and greets them with a motion of his hand, then he takes out of his pocket a bunch of keys and with a solemn gesture sets about opening the door to the new hall.

They enter the old movie house, which has been used for years as a room for the Communist Party's customary meetings. They find frightfully dirty. Hanging on the stage are red cloths, posters, banners. In one corner there is even a statue of Stalin made of papier-mâché.

"What are we going to do with this?"

Mietek, the sad clown, with a comic gesture puts it on his shoulder and carries it away, while the others hum a funeral march. They quickly put the place in order.

The professor walks around the stage, then begins assigning each one his part, as he once did.

"Before beginning," he says, "let's recite some verses from the 'Liberation.' Let's consecrate this hole in the ground with a poem."

They hear something moving from the far end. Someone has entered the hall, but in the dark they can't make out who it is.

"Who is it?" says the professor.

A figure comes forward in long strides toward the stage and appears in the light. It is a priest.

"Karol, it's you! You've come!" exclaims the professor.

He is on the verge of emotion but quickly turns it into a joke:

"And late as usual!"

"The blessing of God is never too late," Karol says from the audience area with a deep voice.

"Then give us a blessing. But don't you think we're too old to begin all over again?"

"Life, in God, is one whole beginning. You begin just as I begin my daily mass: In the name of the Father and the Son and of the Holy Ghost."

The professor makes the sign of the cross:

"But you know how the mass ends; we, instead—."

"We know it, too," says Mietek, the jester.

"How?"

"That we're all going to end up behind bars again!"

A new life for Tadek. He takes down from the bookcase the now useless works that have accumulated there during his period of "errors and deviations." Piled up on the floor are the works of Stalin, the Great Soviet Encyclopedia, the novels of socialist realism, the anthologies of poems on peace. Little Janka, nicknamed Janecka, now five years old, enters the room.

"Daddy, what are you doing?"

"I'm throwing out these books."

"But didn't you tell me, 'Don't throw books away, books are our friends'?"

"But there are good friends and bad friends. These books we're going to send to the paper mill. They'll use them to make new paper. That way they can make better books."

"Daddy, do we always have to get rid of one book to make another book?"

"Not all the time. But this time we do."

"And what about the books *you* wrote? Do you have to get rid of *those* books to make other books?"

"Janecka," blurts Tadek, "go play in your room and don't bother me!"

Janka goes away. A little later, Wanda enters her room. The little girl is throwing her books on the floor.

"What are you doing?"

90

"I'm throwing them away! I want new books, too! Like Daddy."

Wanda picks her up from the floor and carries her into Tadek's room. The man is perched on a step ladder, close to the ceiling and he is reading. His wife inquires:

"What are you reading?"

"My report on Nowa Huta."

"Do you like it?"

Tadek throws it down, saying:

"How can I continue to write as though these books didn't exist? Everything ought to have unity: history, life, literary activity. But when something is broken, there's no more unity. How do you go back and rebuild it?"

With a kiss, Wanda sends Janecka to the bathroom to wash her hands. Tadek now has need of his wife. He gets down from the step ladder and takes her into his arms. She speaks to him tenderly:

"The professor assigned us our parts like before. He told us, 'Let's begin over.' Do it this way. You, too. Simply. Start from the beginning. And trust yourself, in your desire to do good, just like you wanted to do it back then."

"And if you make a mistake again?"

"Today, 'someone' told us that life is one whole beginning."

It is autumn at Nowa Huta. In the place where the cabins used to be, a group of men are digging a hole. Nearby is a large wooden cross ready to be set up. There is also a pamphlet that announces the building of a church dedicated to the Blessed Lady, the Queen of Poland, Marian who has removed his cassock, is working with the others. Among the men is Staszek, now eighteen years old, and among the women is his old grandmother. Staszek digs the hole enthusiastically, but his attention is attracted by a group of girls. He likes one of them very much. Marian straightens up. He drops his shovel and says:

"Okay, fellows, that's fine. The hole is deep enough. Let's stop a minute. Then we can put the cross up."

The men are seated around. From that point one can see how extensive the city is. The buildings, all the same, are lined up as far as the eye can see, and in the background are the patterns of the smoking chimneys and the outlines of the industrial plants. Staszek reaches the girl. He sits down beside her and speaks:

"What's your name?"

"Magda."

"Where are you from? I never saw you before."

"From Cracow."

"This is Cracow here."

"But I come from the old one. I go to the polytechnical institute."

"How come you came here?"

"I came with these friends of mine (she beckons about her) to help put up the cross."

"How did you find out about it?"

"From my 'uncle'."

"Your uncle?"

"Yes, that's what we call him. He's our priest—a pretty unusual guy, but easy to get along with. He always comes with us up the mountain."

"Our priest gets around, too. Otherwise I wouldn't be here. Also because my grandmother asked me to come."

"And why wouldn't you have come?"

"Because," he says seriously, like an eighteen-year-old philosopher, "as a matter of principle, I'm not a believer."

"My 'uncle,' in these cases, usually asks: What do you believe in?"

"I believe in progress and science!"

The conversation is suddenly interrupted by an order from Marian:

"Come on, let's get to work, people of God!"

With a number of "heave hos!" spaced out and rhythmic, the cross slowly goes up. Staszek and Magda work hard. Sweat rolls down their foreheads. They are next to each other. Taking hold of the cross, their hands touch.

Months later, on a day in early spring, under a resplendent sun, a group of skiers climb a snowy slope on the way from Siwe Sady, on the eastern Tatra Mountains. At the head is Father Karol Wojtyla, a professor in Cracow and Lublin, the "uncle" of the studious youth. The group reaches the top of the slope and stops to admire the expanse of white peaks. They are all young. Their enthusiasm is sky-high.

Wojtyla draws back a bit, removes his skis, sits down on a boulder, taken from his knapsack a breviary and begins reciting it in a low voice. The others remove their mountain sacks, take out provisions, divide them up, smoke cigarettes.

Magda approaches the priest, holding a chocolate bar that was already open. Since his back is turned, she taps him on the shoulder:

"'Uncle,' would you like some candy?"

Wojtyla remains in silence and signals no with his head. The girl realizes he was praying, that she has disturbed him, and quickly says, "I'm sorry." She moves away a few steps.

A little later, the priest calls her back with a gesture of the hand. A conversation takes place between them in an undertone. Then Magda returns to the group.

"What did he tell you?" asks a girl friend.

"He inquired about Staszek. I told him he's an atheist."

"And what did he say?"

"He said that, if he really loves me, if he loves me sincerely, he has to love me just as I am, with my thoughts, my feelings, my faith. Because that's what love is. But I too have to love him just as he is, with his lack of faith, with his searching. Not only that, but I have to help him in his searching."

One of the boys approaches the priest. They talk for a moment. Then Wojtyla takes up his breviary, refastens the ski bindings to his boots, and says:

"Okay, people, let's go down!"

One after the other, they dig in with their ski poles, approach the slope, swiftly zigzag their way down it, raising a spray of snow behind them.

In the ups and downs of the relations between church and state in Poland, the brief times when tension ceased alternated with sudden periods of obstinacy. The political establishment feared the Great Adversary, despite her decisive contribution to the unity and stability of the country, and, owing to rivalry and opposing doctrine, was hostile toward her. So it happened at the beginning of 1958, after the breather of the two previous years.

One morning at dawn, in the apartment of the Zapala family in Nowa Huta, Wladek's wife prepares breakfast in the kitchen for her husband. Wladek has already put on his heavy-lined work jacket and now puts on his rubber boots. Just over forty, he is a robust man, tough, with a walrus mustache. Among the workers of the steel mills he is a big shot.

"So they put you on the scraper again! Don't they have any younger men?" asks his wife.

"It's only for today. Then I'll go back to ore."

"And what's so special about today?"

"We have to do some leveling on the Bienczow road."

"Can't they do it without you?"

"Those on the committee asked me to do it," he fumes. "There's no use discussing it!"

His old mother, who has been eavesdropping at the door, comes into the kitchen, wearing her outmoded peasant clothes, and she reproaches her son:

"When those from the committee give orders, it's pretty high and holy, isn't it? Listen to me. There's no leveling to do, Wladek. Don't get mixed up in these things!"

"You'd be better off if you didn't talk nonsense, Ma," retorts Wladek. "In the party you need discipline. When they ask you to go, you have to go."

"Even if they ask you to go kill your wife?"

"You're talking nonsense, Ma!"

"Do you think I don't know it's all about? It's the cross!"

"And they even gave permission for it," says his wife.

"Apparently not for that place," says Wladek, "or else they revoked it..."

Staszek appears at the door. With his hair dishveled, his eyes still swollen nearly shut, he hasn't finished dressing yet:

"They have no right to revoke it. The site location of the church was approved."

"They'll ask permission from you!" replies Wladek angrily. He puts into his ample pockets the bread that was already wrapped in paper, scornfully repeats the dignified word "site location" and leaves without saying goodbye.

The old mother ties a kerchief around her head and hastens outside without saying a word, to the surprise of her daughter-in-law and nephew.

A little later, she arrives at the cross. Other people, mostly women, are already gathered there. A truck pulls up from the distance, full of workers carrying picks and shovels. Behind them slowly moves an enormous scraper. The two vehicles pull up close to the cross, the workers jump out with their tools in hand, the scraper stops a short way off.

The workers look with uncertainty at the crowd assembled around the cross. A squad leader wearing a beret shouts to the people:

"Get out of the way!"

The voice of a woman from the crowd answers:

"*You* get out of the way! What did you come here for?"

Shouts rise up:

"Go away! No one touches the cross."

The man does not yield:

"Get out of the way! Don't create confusion. Let us pass by without any trouble!"

The squad leader motions to the driver of the scraper. Wladek puts the caterpillar tracks in motion and heads toward the cross. But the women move in front of him. Someone intones the hymn "We Want God," and all the people join in to sing. The scraper stops. The workers remain motionless, indecisive.

"Break up the crowd!" shouts the squad leader.

With a bound he manages to avoid a brick that sails past his head. Stones and bricks begin to fly. The workers crouch down behind the truck. The scraper is hit on the sides and the cabin.

Wladek's wife is in the entrance hall to the first-aid station, waiting for her husband. The door opens and Wladek comes out with his head bandaged. The woman runs up to him:

"Did they give you any stitches?"

"Yeah, but it's nothing!"

"Oh, my God!"

"C'mon! Let's get out of here."

Racing by on the street is a convoy of police vans with sirens blaring. The people stop to look.

Wladek's wife expresses her concern.

"What are you complaining about? Do you want to go there? Then go!" rebukes her husband, gesturing with his head to the place where the police are heading.

A few nights later, in the office of the youth organization (Union of Socialist Youth) of the neighborhood of Nowa Huta, in the usual resounding and dismal setting, sit the person in charge of the neighborhood committee and a girl wearing a white blouse and red scarf. He sips tea, while she skims through letters. Staszek, with his hands in his pockets, walks back and forth in front of the table, then he stops and addresses them:

"What's the purpose of all this? Once they gave the permission, they should have..."

"When they gave the permission, that was another situation. Now it's different," explains the man in charge. The girl interposes.

"They made a mistake in doing it in broad daylinght. They should have come at night and that would have solved the problem."

"But the people want the church!" shouts Staszek.

"What stupid people!" is the judgment of the man in charge. The girl says:

"They're peasants from the countryside. The priests have been instigating them and maybe not only the priests."

"I come from the countryside, too!" says Staszek boldly.

"What are you talking about?"

"They split my father's head open with a brick."

"There, you see? They're really stupid," shrieks the girl.

Staszek puts his fists on the table. He is about to explode. Then suddenly he realizes that it is impossible to reason with these people. He quickly turns around, heads for the door and leaves.

A few days later, late one evening. Getting off at the trolley stops are workers on the way back from the industrial plants. Between those who get off and passersby, blunt and lively conversations take place. The people are excited, making gesticulations. They form into groups that hasten in the same direction: they are going to the place of the cross. The crowd swells. In the opposite direction, in the center of the street, an ambulance speeds by, with sirens blaring. Gradually as they approach, the people can hear the strains of religious songs. Then the songs give way to agitated shouts. The cross is lit up by a convergence of automobile lights: they are the blinding lights of police vans. The crowd begins to undulate, pressed and beaten by the guardians of the law.

Staszek, wearing his best clothes, enters the building of the Regional Committee of the Communist Party in Cracow. He shows his card to the "admittance" officer, walks up the stairs, reaches the secretary's office, knocks and enters, somewhat timidly. The secretary, remaining seated, points to an armchair. Staszek sits down.

"Are you from the Union of Socialist Youth of Nowa Huta? Did they send you with some resolution?"

"No, comrade secretary. I came on my own."

"Here I am. What's it about?"

"About the things going on."

"Do you have some information to give me?"

"I tried to persuade the comrades to send a delegation, but they wouldn't have it. So I took it on myself..."

"Took it on yourself? What?"

"Comrade! They're really taking a beating there. It's been three days now. There are people wounded, in jail."

"Some pretty interesting news you brought me, right? But what did you think, that the revolution was only made up of idle talk and newspaper articles?"

"What good does all this do?"

Staszek is full of courage and righteous indignation.

96

"The people," he says, "are all worked up..."

"Listen!" says the secretary, interrupting him. "Nowa Huta must be a socialist city. The first socialist city in Poland. There's no room for a church."

"Then why did they give permission for it?"

"Well, you see... at times we make errors, too."

"Giving permission was an error, then?" Staszek cannot believe his ears.

"And what do *you* think about it?" says the secretary provokingly.

"Comrade secretary, most of the people are believers. The Constitution does not forbid them to go to church."

"No one is forbidding them. They can go whenever they like. Aren't there a lot of churches in Cracow? Anyone can take the trolley car and go. And then, just a few steps away they have the Church of the Holy Cross of Mogila with the good Cistercian monks always at their disposal. No, don't let them make you believe that we're persecuting religion!"

Staszek wavers. The secretary's arguments have him backed up in a corner of the ring. He does seem to have one argument though:

"I'm not saying it's not this way. But when you first promise poeple something and then forbid them to have it, then..."

"You know what I say?" the comrade interrupts. "You have to have a little imagination. Those people who today are fighting for the cross with shovels and stones are people who are still tied to the cassocks of the country priests. But new generations are growing up. It's just a matter of time. Pretty soon the churches won't be of use to anyone. There won't be any more priests. The people will find out for themselves just where the truth is. Where do *you* come from? Do you come from the country?"

"From the country, near Kalwaria."

"Do you have a farm?"

"My father had five acres."

"You see? He now has a house with a bathroom, central heating, and a good job. You're probably studying..."

"Yes, mining engineering."

"There! Who gave you all this? The church or the democratic authorities?"

"I know, I understand, but..."

On the desk a telephone rings. The secretary answers:

"Yes? He's already arrived? Send him to me. I'll see him right away."

Staszek gets up. The secretary gets up also, moves, in front of the desk, comes close to him and says:

"So what you're trying to say is that our politics are no good..."

He pats him on the back, gently pushes him to the door, while he continues his final monologue:

"Believe me, we've had a bit of experience! And if there are other activists there like you, tell your friends that we can do without them."

The door opens. A corpulent dignitary enters the room. The secretary focuses all his attention on him, with effusive embraces and greetings. Staszek slinks out, humiliated and downcast, without saying a word.

The brutal repression at Nowa Huta has wounded the priestly heart of Marian. He decides to go to the Archbishop's residence in Cracow, to talk about it with Bishop Baziak. The best time to meet him, without the risk of missing him for the umpteenth time, owing to his continual and pressing pastoral schedule, is to get to him right after the rite of ordination of the new auxiliary Bishop, which will be taking place in Wawel on Sunday, September 28, 1958. He goes up the hill and enters the cathedral packed with people, at the moment when the new Bishop, at the end of the ceremony, walks slowly down the nave of the temple vested with the accouterments of the new order, with miter and crosier. Marian can't see his face, which is hidden from the crowd. But he does see the miter swaying above the heads and notes the unusual atmosphere that reigns in the famous basilica. Bustling about the new Bishop are moslty young people, boys and girls. The Bishop embraces and kisses everyone, with the simplicity and familiarity of an old friend who knows each individual person and each of whom he loves beyond measure. Suddenly the priest sees that the Bishop's hand is free. He presses hard between the Bishop's fingers a pair of rosary beads, just as the boy had done one evening at the hospital in Solvay, with his head and face hidden by bandages.

Great changes were taking place in the church. In 1958, Pius XII died, after a pontificate that lasted a little less than twenty years, with an arduous war and postwar period. Pope Eugenio Pacelli had directed the church with great wisdom and left it an enormous body of doctrinal teaching. The impression he gave as Angelic Pastor was indelible in the hearts of millions of people. He was succeeded by John XXIII, Angelo Giuseppe Roncalli, who in less than five years captured the affection and admiration of the world, showing a humanity and wisdom redolent of an ancient patriarch. The focal point of his pontificate was the convocation of the Second Vatican Ecumenical Council, which would give a total revision of the church's activity, in the face of a world reality completely different from that of centuries past. The torch lit by him passed on, after his death in 1963, into the hands of Paul VI, Giovanni Battista Montini, who continued on with and concluded the Council, later instituting the Synod of Bishops, a consultative body of the Pope, consisting of representatives of the episcopate throughout the world, which periodically meets in Roma.

During the Council, the young Bishop from Cracow played an active role, which put him in the spotlight, owing to his brilliant interventions in the eyes of the world episcopate. After the Council, his name would be one of the most voted upon for election of the members of the Synod of Bishops.

At the end of the third session of the Council, November 11, 1964, Pope Paul VI was told of the Bishop's desire to build a church in Nowa Huta. With one of the gestures typical of his keen sensitivity, he gave the Bishop a stone taken from the diggings in the Vatican Basilica, to serve as the first stone of the new building.

The stick-to-itiveness of the people from the satellite city of Cracow, fully bolstered by the Metropolitan Archbishop, wrested permission from the political authorities. It was granted on October 13, 1967. The project of a city without God had failed. Immediately work began, leading to the construction of a big church, modern in architecture, impressive for its originality, laid out on the inside in three open and intercommunicating levels, dominated by a gigantic Christ crucified, modeled in bronze, aerodynamic, with the corpus leaning forward to symbolize an infinite surge of love.

It is a cold winter night. In the windows of many buildings, one can see the multicolor lights of the Christmas trees. Many people gather inside and around the recently erected foundations of the new church. They are no longer only the faithful of Nowa Huta or the active groups defending the Faith who had kept lit for years the flame of hope. Now they come also from Cracow, and there come also those who in the beginning were skeptic or indifferent.

Between the foundations of the church, everything is ready for the celebration of the mass. Marian, with a white surplice over his coat, moves about the altar, which only the wooden scaffolding protects from the sleet that flutters in the air. The congregation sings Christmas hymns. Amid the crows proceeds a figure dressed in scarlet: it is the Cardinal Archbishop Wojtyla, who is coming to celebrate Christmas with a Jesus who doesn't yet have a roof over His head, among His children who have waited for so long to be able to give Him one. While the chorus of voices intones *Ecce Sacerdos Magnus!*, Wojtyla clasps hands, caresses heads, embraces and greets hundreds of people, his brethren and his friends.

The mass begins. Among the crowd is Magda, now a woman, come from Cracow with a group of friends to hear their "uncle," who for four years has been the head of the entire Catholic community of the archdiocese.

Magda feels someone trying to embrace her. She turns. It is Staszek. He whispers in her ear: "I love you." Magda fells embarrassed and at the same time overwhelmed with joy. They pray together.

"The grace of Our Lord Jesus Christ, the love of God the Father and the communion of the Holy Spirit be with you all," says the stern voice of Wojtyla.

"And with you also."

Magda answers together with the congregation, with understandable heightened emotion. But when Staszek, in his enthusiasm, attempts to give her a kiss, she elbows him aside.

"Are you crazy? In church?"

"Excuse me," he says adroitly. "I thought I was back on Kasprowy."

The dizzy summit of the Tatra Mountains, which Staszek is alluding to, brings back sweet memories and symbolizes the level of their aspirations.

The deacon reads the Gospel according to Saint Luke:

"In those days Emperor Augustus ordered a census taken of the whole world... Joseph also went up from the town of Nazareth in Gaililee to David's town, called Bethlehem, in Judea, because he was one of the descendants of David, to register with Mary, his bride, who was going to have a child. And while they were there, the time came for her to have her child. She had her firstborn son, and she wrapped him up and laid him in a manger because there was no one room for them in the inn."

Archbishop Wojtyla begins to address them. He stands bareheaded under the wintry sky, within the barely laidout perimeter of the new walls, in the site of that city of work, which looks at him through the windows and from the balconies thronged with people all bundled up, and which seem to thank him for the courage he showed in defending with so great tenacity their just cause and for having come to be with them on the most earthquaking night of the year.

"The church that is now rising up here is the fruit of your prayers," he says. "You, here out in the open, standing or kneeling, have prayed, just as for months and years you prayed and suffered, giving proof of your faith, with firm behavior, dignified, sure of your own rights. I would like to say to Jesus: Look, O Christ, at how rich You've become! How many people came to visit You on the night of Your birth in Bethlehem? And look at how many have come to Nowa Huta to celebrate Your Polish Bethlehem."

100

The Uphill Road to Freedom

In the spring of 1968, the tension which had accumulated throughout Polish soviety for political, economic, social and religious reasons, erupted into a series of student riots which beset the major universities of the country. There was a loud outcry for civil rights and the only response, other than immediate repression, was in the form of an anti-revisionist and anti-Zionist campaign unleashed by the authorities and consisting of a series of purges against people of rank, figures in the cultural world and public administration who were of Jewish origin or identified as Marxist revisionists.

Between 1968 and 1969, Poland was to see the exodus of more than ten thousand people who were forced to emigrate because of the turn in the public fortunes. Their names included people of considerable prestige. At the root of these developments were the so-called "March uprisings."

One evening, late at night, in the large market square in Cracow, a crowd of students gathers around the floodlit Adam Mickiewicz monument whose base is covered with flowers. A student who has climbed on the pedestal harangues his fellow students, but his words are lost in the general babble and chatter. Everyone argues and gesticulates under the banners recently hoisted and bearing the libertarian slogans: "The papers lie!" "Down with

101

censorship!'' ''Bread is nothing without freedom!'' This time, too, the Rynek Glowny is carefully watched by police squadrons awaiting orders. Suddenly, the policemen slowly move in toward the crowd.

Early the next morning, in the home of Wladek at Nowa Huta, the day starts with a hearty breakfast. Wladek wears a new armband—it bears the letters ORMO (Auxiliary Police Vulunteers). His wife spreads butter on the bread when Staszek enters, apparently ready to go out.

''Where are you going?'' his father asks.

''To the polytechnic.''

''What are you going to do there? All your friends are out on strike!''

''I have to be with them.''

His mother interjects:

''What's the point? You'll get beaten up!''

''And you, Dad, where are you going?'' asks Staszek defiantly.

''Where am I going? To do my duty!''

''With this?'' And so saying, he pulls out from under the chair a large piece of metal cable in the shape of a club.

''Everyone has been given one,'' says Wladek, embarrassed.

''To beat up the students, right?''

''You don't have to use it if you don't want to. It's just so as to get respect and frighten them a little.''

''Do you want to frighten me?''

''You're not going anywhere! I haven't worked all my life just to see you thrown out of the university for this nonsense!''

Wladek's wife helps him out by reminding their son of the advantages he will obtain by completing his course of studies, which is drawing to a close, following which he will become a university professor. But Staszek does not agree at all:

''Is that all that matters? What about Poland?''

''What do you know about Poland? Did you fight in the war, by any chance? Did you help to build it up? It's easy to distort things...'' his mother retorts heatedly.

''It's also easy to browbeat people with an iron cable! Dad, they've already set you against people once...''

He turns toward the door, but his mother blocks the way:

''Don't go, Staszek!''

The young man avoids her and goes out, loudly slamming the door after him. Wladek immediately falls into a deep silence, his face darkening, and he even pushes away the steaming cup of coffee in front of him. A few minutes later the quiet of the morning air is shattered by the sound of a horn. Wladek's friends have arrived in their truck and are waiting to pick him up and drive off with him. His wife urges him to make haste and go downstairs. The man gets up and goes toward the door, then turns and sits down again. Something has broken inside him. The horn sounds again, impatiently.

"I'm not going!" Wladek shouts to his wife.

"Go! You will bring Staszek home."

"Let him go where he wants!" With these words, he angrily tears off his armband.

The police surround the students who are setting fire to the newspapers and shouting: "The papers lie, we want the truth!"

There is a full-scale attack. Tear bombs rain all over the square. Hydrants are opened and aimed at the students, while civilians, wearing armbands and carrying clubs, grab and beat the demonstrators. Staszek is close to Magda, protecting her and trying to remove her from the square. They cough and their eyes are red and tearing. The assailants unleash violent blows. Suddenly, Magda is caught up in the jostle, carried far from Staszek and viciously clubbed by an auxiliary. Boys and girls are beaten blindly, Many are loaded on to trucks and driven away.

Staszek returns home late that evening. He bears the marks of the battle which lasted almost all day: bruises on his face, tears in his clothing. He rings the doorbell and his father opens the door in his pajamas.

"Staszek, what's happened?" he says, agitated at seeing him like that.

Staszek gives full vent to his anger:

"You thought you could frighten people, didn't you, you scum. Magda has been battered black and blue. You're all scum, all of you!"

"Silence!" his father orders. Staszek has lost all self-control. He throws himself upon him and punches him. A struggle ensues which frightens the women and leaves the two combatants bedraggled and humiliated. Sobbing, Staszek withdraws to his room.

"What are you doing to each other?" shouts Wladek's wife.

"He has struck his father!" he says, gravely.

And the grandmother adds in a firm tone:

"That's what happens when children are raised without God."

In a room at the Cracow University, under gilt frames encompassing the portraits of illustrious masters of former times, pompously garbed in violet and crimson robes with ermine collars, Jozek is striding nervously before the enormous council table where an elderly professor is seated.

"It's over for me. It's all over!"

"Don't exaggerate. Certainly, the police use violent tactics to break us up, as if we were scoundrels!"

"The students will adore you for having defended them so courageously," Jozek tells him, with sincerity.

"You defended them, too! The police even snatched your bag from you hand."

"It's different for me. They won't have time to adore me. Have you seen the papers today? Have you read about the attacks against Zionism? They don't dare to speak of Semitism anymore. They don't have the nerve to attack the Jews again so brazenly. Now they've come up with this new term which gives them a convenient pretext—Zionism, the Jews' desire to return to their fatherland and there defend the independence of their people—this allegedly is the new threat facing the world. And what will be the consequence? A new attack against the Jews."

"But you, what harm have you done?"

"It makes no difference. Now they're starting to look for a scapegoat for the disorders of the last few days. Do you know the story of the pharoah and the Jewish doctor? The one who prescribed an enema for the pharoah? The pharoah was so outraged that he made the doctor have the enema. Ever since then whenever a king feels sick, he orders an enema to be administered to all the Jews."

"My dear colleague, you're becoming a masochist," the senior professor tells him.

"Not at all. I am just continuing to be what I am—a historian."

"And as a Marxist historian, were you able to foresee such a course of events?"

"Not entirely foresee. But, at least since 1956, I have been noticing a disquieting divergence between theory and practice. Unfortunately, history does not confine itself, and frequently does not adhere to theoretical conjecture."

"And what conclusion have you reached?"

"Not the one you think. I have not lost faith in Marxism. I only have doubts about the Marxist state. But that will not cause me to abandon my research as a Marxist scholar in this country."

The professor frowns, repeating emphatically:

"—in this country!"

104

"Yes! In my country. I shall never leave it. Not even if they try to force me to do so."

Neither the repression of the student protests nor the search for scapegoats among the so-called revisionists and Zionists prevented new demonstrations. In 1970 there was a workers' revolt on the Baltic coast. In Danzig, Gdynia and Stettin the workers went out on strike.

In December of that year, the workers in the shipyard, showing their rejection of the government's attempts in 1968 to set workers against students, rebelled against the institutions, asking for more bread and more freedom. As is usually the case, the repression was implacable. The official count was fifty-six dead and several hundred wounded. But the actual toll was much heavier. The party secretary, Wladislaw Gomulka, was forced to resign. He was succeeded by Edward Gierek, who in January of 1971 personally visited all the industrial complexes in the Baltic, talking with the workers and making promises. But the discontent continued to spread and it erupted again in 1976, at the end of June. The Ursus tractor factory, twenty-five kilometers from Warsaw, and the arms manufacturing industry in Radom, one hundred kilometers from Warsaw, were the tinder-boxes of a new rebellion, triggered by the refusal to accept the price increase decided by the government for such staples as butter and meat, but immediately fueled by the loud demands for political and union reforms. The revolt was suppressed at the cost of several dead and the dismissal of enormous numbers of workers who had been outspoken in their activism.

Meanwhile, however, the secret fabric of social pluralism was gaining strength, undermining the numbing monolithism demanded by the party. A committee of intellectuals was born which promised to defend the workers and help them they were fired or black-listed for political reasons. An anti-totalitarian resistance movement was founded to fight on many fronts. A mobile university was set up for workers and ousted students, supported by the unselfish dedication of all the great names in Polish culture. A movement for the defense of the right of the individual and of the citizen was born. It received the full support of the two leaders of the church in Poland, Cardinals Wyszynski and Wojtyla. Later, in 1977, in the wake of the revitalization movement of the Polish middle classed and inspired by the previous revolts, the first active intelligentsia was formed and, particularly in Danzig and Katowice, it prepared the way for the free union charter committees. Meanwhile, the organizers, concerned about how to educate the workers in unions, set up constructive relations with the intellectuals and formed underground publications.

Meanwhile, two events of incalculable scope took place. The Cardinal Archbishop of Cracow, Karol Wojtyla, was elected to the papacy and subsequently visited Poland. These represented two psychological tremors which shook with incredible force and caused the Poles to rediscover their ability to act individually and collectively against the widespread sense of resignation which the social order had infused into most of the citizenry. Furthermore, throughout the entire Polish experience there had remained in the background, ever since 1948, the unflinching and peerlessly authoritative figure of Primate Cardinal Wyszynski, the Archbishop of Gniezno and Warsaw.

In Poland, the year 1977 was one of frantic activity for all those who sought greater freedom and more participation in social affairs, while still respecting the laws and loyalty to the state's institutions.

In the Dominican convent in Cracow, a large number of people arranged to meet for what appeared to be a religious ritual, but which was actually an enlightened exchange of ideas on the emergency of the social situation.

Both cloister and church were invaded by a silent crowd taking its normal and makeshift seats provided by the dynamic white-robed monks bustling about, carrying chairs and benches.

Magda and Staszek are standing at the door of the church, waiting for someone. It is still winter. It is snowing and the temperature is below zero. The young couple huddle in their overcoats and rub their freezing hands. At last, the person they are waiting for emerges from the crowd: a young man, with a hurried air and lost in thought. Staszek calls out to him and helps him to shake off the snow which has stuck on him just about everywhere, even in his eyes, and urges him into the cloister. From underneath his coat he draws out a few copies of a large, neatly packaged opus and hands it to the man.

"Here's the book. The work is rather rough, not all the pages have come out clear because duplicator we were able to use was rather antiquated."

"But it's magnificent!" exclaims Tadeusz, the man they have been waiting for. "And it's a real book!"

"You've published nicer things in the past," Staszek says to him as if to console him.

"No, this is the best! Partly because I think that it's a good book."

"We have sold all the copies in one go," says Magda.

"When? Where?" asks Tadek.

"Today, here at the entrance, and they were not enough."

Tadek enters the church, sees the people holding his book, and is overcome at the idea of having to speak before such a learned and committed audience. But Magda hastens to bolster his courage:

"It is you they have come to hear, because they know what it cost you to reach this point, but they also know that they can count on you for clear ideas."

One morning in Nowa Huta, a crowd of workers from the first shift heads for the steel factory. The smoke from the chimneys seem to congeal in the icy air and the people's breath hangs like a continuous cloud over the rivers of humanity converging toward the work place, trudging through the frozen snow.

Wladek is among them. With his heavy-set body and strong hands he advances with measured steps, his thick moustache projecting from his handsome, ruddy face. He absent-mindedly strokes the scar on his cheek which marks the beginning of his new destiny: for it was the shot fired by the German beneath the farmhous in Kalwaria which first drove him underground and opened to him a new world, one in which he developed a taste for more exciting relations than those possible in the solitary countryside to which he was accustomed. If it were not for that, he would still be there, although he does return there punctually on Good Friday every year, to carry the cross in the Passion play, just like his father and ancestors.

As he does every morning, he enters the front hall of the big factory, approaches the board showing the workers cards used for the daily clocking-in and clocking-out, reaches up for his card and finds the slot empty. He turns to the guard on duty for an explanation, but the guard sends him to the boss. In the big shed adjoining the furnaces, the wagons carrying the iron ore have come to a stop. The workers on duty are standing around, their arms folded, silently smoking and waiting.

"Why isn't this convoy moving?" shouts an engineer in charge of that department. No one answers. They all remain silent, as if they hadn't heard.

"What is it? A strike?"

"When our foreman gets back, then we'll work," is the reply.

Then the engineer says in a conciliatory tone:

"You know that he is not coming back. He's been transferred."

"Transferred or thrown out?" interjects a worker.

"Thrown out!" his companions echo, angrily.

"You know very well that management has the right to transfer of fire employees," the engineer continues.

"Yes, when there's a valid reason," the workers retort.

"Obviously, he was not functioning," comments the engineer, cynically.

The men draw around him threateningly.

"He'd been working here right from the start! You could even say that it was he that built the steelworks! And you, how long have you been working here?"

The engineer, getting nervous, takes a few steps back, then, believing that he can wield his authority, says:

"You can't argue here!"

"Of course we can't argue here," echo the workmen. "Just put the nose to the grindstone and work! Isn't that right? Zapala was protesting, he was demanding his rights! Sundays off, wages adjusted to the cost of living, family allowances, human working hours! That's why you got rid of him!"

"There are unions to handle these questions," answers the engineer, nervously. But all he elicits is bitter laughter.

"Yes, the unions, your unions. Bosses!"

"So, are you going to get to work, yes or no?"

The workers say nothing.

"All right. We'll discuss this at another time!" And with this veiled threat, he walks away.

In the manager's office in the Nowa Huta steel factory, a small group of executives is receiving orders. Suddenly, without warning, Wladek bursts in excitedly, his face red.

"I can guarantee that you can't do it! I'll apply to the Court of Labor!" he blurts out to his superior whom, for the first time, he now looks at openly with contempt and disdain.

"I wouldn't advise that," the other replies. "The union leaders have spoken with all you men, with each of them separately, and they have all admitted that you incited them to strike, that you threw the labor organization into disarray."

"That's impossible! Or else you forced it out of them! If I had been present they would have spoken differently. Come with me and talk with them, come and talk to people in the factory."

"There's no reason," the manager says coldly.

"Then I'll call them!"

He moves toward the intercom on the boss's table, grabs the microphone and shouts: "Ore transport furnace gang! This is Wladek Zapala. Come out into the yard."

The manager shakes his head in a gesture of long-suffering:

"You don't even know how to make it work!"

108

The police search Wladek's house. The man has fallen into disgrace and consequently he is suspected of antigovernment activities. The women watch in dismay as the uniformed men turn the place upside down. The men say nothing. Staszek sits on a couch, feigning indifference. But the officers make him get up so they can search under the cushions. They find a bag, exactly where the young man was sitting and, opening it, they draw out large numbers of duplicated manuscripts.

"What's this stuff?" one of them asks.

"Didn't they teach you to read?" answers Wladek, coldly.

"Books printed secretly," the policeman says gravely, "without the censor's authorization. And flyers, too! Its says: 'Anniversary Mass for the Danzig strikers.' This is prohibited material, this is activity against the state. Who here is responsible for the presence of this material?"

"It's mine!" says Staszek.

"No, they're mine!" Wladek blurts out.

"Papa..."

"Don't interrupt when your father is talking. I went to get this material and I've distributed it whereve I could. I want people to remember what the workers have done."

"Kindly come with me to the police headquarters."

On May 15, 1977, after almost ten years of work, the church of Nowa Huta is ready for consecration. Now Marian can officiate in peace every day, and people are flocking, particularly on Sundays, to the masses and holy sacraments. It is a day in mid-December, the anniversary of the Danzig uprising. Marian is celebrating a suffrage mass for the slain, and the crowds fill the various levels in the church which seem to be bursting with humanity. Robed in his vestments of purple mourning, Marian speaks to the people:

"On the anniversary of the tragic events of Danzig and Gdynia in December 1970, I want to recall a few words recently spoken by our pastor, Cardinal Karol Wojtyla: 'The workers, the laborers on Polish soil, are a multitude of people who believe in God, friends of Christ who want to love one another. They do not want to hate anyone. But they have a conscience. The conscience of their rights, which are also recognized by the constitution and by the laws of the state. They know that they are entitled to freedom of worship, to religious freedom, to freedom of thought, and they want these basic human rights to be protected in all their scope...'"

Wladek is among the people listening to him, ecstatic, together with his wife, his old mother, Staszek and Magda.

The Relentless Climb

Cardinal Wojtyla is at the Vatican, giving a sermon on spiritual exercises. It is the first week of Lent in 1976. Paul VI called him to this prestigious and grave act of ministry when he was in the middle of his pastoral activity, weighed down by concern and commitments. He had just two weeks to prepare the vast amount of material necessary to conduct as much as twenty-two sermons before the Pope and his closest and highest-ranked collaborators.

Accompanied by Marian, he crosses the ancient and picturesque courtyard of San Damaso, takes the elevator to the second loggia of the apostolic palace, and enters the Matilde Chapel. The prelates sit in the pews with seats lined in red velvet, in the chapel which has been completely renovated at the wish of Paul VI. The walls are covered with sober, pastel-grey velvet and two splendid Flemish tapestries depicting scenes from the Gospel. In front are the stone altar, the tabernacle and a bas-relief of Christ from the early Christian era.

The Pope is absorbed in prayer on the *prie-dieu* (a piece of furniture for kneeling on while praying) placed just inside the entrance to the tiny Oratory of San Lorenzo located on the right side of the altar. He is no visible to anyone sitting in the pews, but he is to the preacher who is weaving, so to speak, his spiritual dialogue with that of the Pope, with that much beloved Pope who holds him in such esteem and whom he will one day define, in his first Encyclical, as "great predecessor and true father."

The theme of the exercises selected by Cardinal Wojtyla are the words "Sign of Contradiction," a phrase in the Gospel which refers to Jesus Christ.

It is around the figure and works of the Lord that the deeply spiritual discourse of that week unfolds.

One day, he even speaks of his own town and cathedral. "I would like to begin this meditation with words familiar to you all. They return every year, in the culminating days of the church's liturgy, when we commemorate the Passion, the Death and the Resurrection of our Lord. 'Christ became obedient for us, even unto death,' the church sings during Holy Week..."

"I shall never forget what I felt the first time I heard these words during the solemn liturgy that was conducted in the Royal Cathedral of Wawel, in Cracow. I was young and I had gone there on the afternoon of Holy Wednesday when they were singing the first 'Matins of Darkness.' I remember the pupils from the seminary seated in the pews, the canons of the chapter in their choir stalls and, near the high altar, on the Bishop's throne, the Archbishop of Cracow, the unforgettable Cardinal Adam Stefan Sapieha. In the center of the presbytery there was the big three-cornered candelabra holding the candles which were extinguished one by one as the singing of each individual psalm was completed. Then, at the end, they sang that memorable phrase of Saint Paul: 'Christ became obedient for us, even unto death'..."

Marian listens to his Cardinal from a remote corner of the Matilde Chapel. He sees the scene at Wawel drift before his eyes as in a dream.

Wojtyla continues: "Even today, I often think of that service, because that first experience was unique, and never again has it returned with the same intensity, not even in the same cathedral during the same annual celebrations. It basically consisted not only of the discovery of the beauty and spiritual enchantment of the liturgy of Holy Week, but above all in the discovery of that absolute dimension which is the mystery expressed in the liturgy which serves to pronounce it as an ever-present message.

"After the words of Saint Paul about Christ's obedience even unto death, everyone remained in deep silence and I felt that at that moment, not only were the people silent but also the entire cathedral, that cathedral which embodied the history of my nation.

"All mankind, the church and the world, the past, present and the future,

112

are united in the deep silence filled with adoration at the fact that 'Christ became obedient for us, even unto death'!..."

As he continues his homily, he goes on to develop the theme as follows: "Justice is a task that must be fulfilled, that constantly reappears to confront every man, every generation. Jesus Christ took this task upon himself and fulfilled it to its roots. Man began to be unjust when he first disobeyed the Creator; this is why Jesus became obedient even unto death, thus bequeathing his justice to man, like an inexhaustible source of justification before God.

"There have been in the past and there still are today so many plans to heal the world, which herald the arrival of a true justice amongst men. But these plans cannot be considered complete if they do not encompass that justification before God which is the primary basis for all justice, to which we have been led by the obedience of Christ, obedience even unto death..."

Before Marian's eyes, Archbishop Sapieha rises from his throne-like seat, beats on the wooden steps three times with his stick, followed by the canons and clergy, who beat on the benches with their books in the ritual that recalls the horror of the world at the killing of the Redeemer. Then the cathedral sinks again into shadowy silence.

On August 6, 1978, after fifteen years of an exceptionally eventful and turbulent pontificate, Pope Paul VI died at Castel Gandolfo. The funeral mass was held in Saint Peter's, the period of mourning was observed, and then the Cardinals locked themselves in conclave in the apostolic palace of the Vatican. On August 26, after twenty-four hours, they elected to the papacy the Patriarch of Venice, Cardinal Albino Luciani, who adopted the names of John and Paul to honor his two predecessors and their historical endeavor to instill new life into the church through the Council.

The new Pope was a true shepherd, an amiable, simple and down-to-earth man whose steady and humble style as ruler of the church won the admiration and affection of the people throughout the world. But after only thirty-three days of papacy, he unexpectedly died at around midnight on September 28 from a heart attack.

In Rome, the ceremonies of the previous month of August were repeated and the Cardinals again withdrew to their conclave on the evening of Saturday the 14th of October to choose a successor to John Paul I.

It is the evening of Monday, October 16, 1978. In the Solvay chemical plant in Cracow, a small engine hauls the little wagons carrying the ore needed for processing for the production of soda. A worker, carrying his helmet in his hand, runs up to the engine driver and shouts: "Have you heard the news?"

The other workmen run over, already aware of the news that has spread throughout Poland like wildfire. They throw their protective helmets into the air excitedly. The engine drive, amazed and almost disbelieving, flips the switch of the sound signal on his engine and, with a very shrill whistle, confirms the astounding news. Almost immediately, the sirens of the plant start to sound, followed by bells and other sirens. Towering over everybody and everything, the powerful and harmonious sound of the historical Sigismonda bell is heard from the top of its tower in Wawel, flooding the entire city. The great factory shuts down. People gather in huddles all over town and speak of nothing else. The Cardinals have chosen their former workmate. Archbishop of Cracrow Karol Wojtyla, as successor to John Paul I. His name will be John Paul II.

In Saint Peter's Square in Rome, after the announcement by the senior Cardinal Deacon, the crowd has become an endless sea of people. They are waiting anxiously to see the new Pope, the first non-Italian after almost five hundred years of uninterrupted tradition. When the chosen candidate appears on the balcony to give the benediction, the ovation is overwhelming. He starts to speak:

"Jesus Christ be praised. Beloved brothers and sisters. We are all still grieving from the death of our most dearly beloved, Pope John Paul I. And now the most eminent Cardinals have called a new Bishop of Rome. They have called him from a distant country... fár away, but always so close in the communion of the Christian faith and tradition. I was afraid to accept this appointment. But I have done so in the spirit of obedience towards our Lord Jesus Christ and in total trust towards his Mother, the most Holy Madonna. I do not know if I can express myself well in your—in our Italian language. If I err, you will correct me. And so I present myself to you all, to confess our common faith, our hope, our trust in the Mother of Christ and of the church, with the help of God and with the help of men."

The great square seems to go mad with excitement and joy.

In Cracow, it is a sultry October evening, which would normally be just like any other. But the town has literally exploded. Through the streets, youths are running carrying torches and flags. In their homes, people chatter, pray, weep, anxiously waiting for more detailed news that might satisfy their enormous curiosity in the historic event.

Tadek throws open the window. He listens a long time to the sound of the Sigismonda and the other bells. In the street, he watches the whirling autumn leaves that have fallen from the trees and are no longer caught up by the wind but by the rushing movement of the sudden processions crying hosannahs. Gradually, his eyes drift from the scene around him and turn toward his inner soul. Behind him are the desk covered with papers, the typewriter and the radio from which he heard the sober but momentous announcement of the news of the century.

Wanda joins him, trembling and moved. They remain silent for a long time together. Both of them see before their eyes the same image of a past both distant and near. Then Wanda speaks:

"Oh Tadek, what's wrong with you? You don't seem happy," she whispers to him.

"Certainly, I am," says Tadek, in a low voice."

"However, there's something that worries you."

"It is... it is that I'm afraid for him. Will they be able to understand all that he has gone through? All that makes him what he is? From now on he will be completely alone."

"Yes, dear, it is true; you are right. But this was his vocation."

"And to think that I had so many things to speak to him about... and now I won't be able to tell him anything of what I had so much at heart."

"True. He won't come back. He will never come back again?"

"And even if he does come back, it will be only to say good-bye."

The sound of the bell of Sigismonda grows louder and louder. It looms like a great giant in its lofty castle of iron beams, rhythmically swaying under the pull of sixteen ropes pulled by sixteen sweating and panting youths. inside the cathedral, the silver urn containing the remains of Saint Stanislaw glimmers in the semi-darkness. In the crypt of Saint Leonard, among the royal sarcophagi, the old vicar of the cathedral is kneeling before the bare stone altar where Karol Wojtyla once celebrating his first mass. His cryes are full of tears. Shaking with emotion and fervor, he mumbles a prayer incoherently but from the bottom of his soul;

"Deus mirabilis... Te Deum laudamus... Deo gratias."

It is Sunday, June 10, 1979, and Pope John Paul II is celebrating a solemn mass in the Blonie, the enormous public lawn in Cracow. He has returned to his fatherland for nine days. He has revisited the most significant spots. As Pope, he has spoken to the beloved Polish people. In his speeches, he has touched all the chords of the Polish soul, all the sentiments, all the important issues affecting his tormented and predestined nation which, in these times, has been called by God to perform an exceptional mission.

On his last day he is in his own Cracow, to embrace again his brothers and sisters and children, to celebrate with them the ninth centenary of the martyrdom of the patron Saint Stanislow, to bring to a close the archdiocesan synod which he began and kept alive for so many years.

His heart overflowing with love, as he has already shown in his many gestures, meetings, greetings, dialogues and hymns, the Polish Pope, the first Slavic Pope in history, exhorts his fellow citizens:

"You must be strong! With that strength which flows from faith! You must be faithful! Today, more than at any other time, you need this strength. You must be strong with the strength of the hope that sustains the perfect joy of living... Before I leave you here, I beg you to accept once again all the spiritual heritage which bears the name Poland, with the faith, hope, and charity which God has grafted in us by his holy baptism."

The mass is very long. The people are happy and enthusiastic. At the communion, Tadek and Wanda approach to receive the Eucharist from the hands of the Pope, together with their Janka, the little girl of many years ago, and then Staszek and Magda, and Wladek with his wife and elderly mother, while Marian, in a white surplice, assists the celebrant.

At the end, the moment of separation arrives. The rumble of the Sigismonda bell which has resumed its toll from Wawel of the solemn hour, resounds through the loudspeakers. Millions of hands stretch out toward the white figure robed in his red mantle, whom everyone longs to embrace. The open smile of the great friend of Cracow and of Poland, now called to be a friend to all mankind, remains, with his arms raised and hands outstretched, the sign of the new security, the new greatness of that extraordinary people.

116

SCENES FROM THE FILM

(Preceding page)
In this house in Wadowice,
near Cracow, Karol Wojtyła
was born on 18 May 1920.

The father of Wojtyła (lower panel
extreme right) and in center with
little Karoł) was a tailor who
stopped his practice in 1900.
Successively, he became a sub-officer
in the army.
Karol Wojtyła as an adult (center panel)
who found his religious vocation in 1940.
On November 1, 1946,
he was ordained priest (top right);
later he became an Auxiliary Bishop,
then Archbishop of Cracow (top left).
Karol Wojtyła as a young priest
with a priest companion
(lower left).

In September 1939
the Germans invaded Poland.
During the occupation they destroyed
the ghettos of Warsaw and Cracow,
and later the whole Warsaw.
The Jews and citizens of the
resistance are deported
to the Concentration Camp (Lager)
of Auschwitz (lower left)
The partisans also contribute
to the liberation attained by
the Red Army (1944) (lower center)
who them mobilize themselves
to reconstruct the Country.

At the Shrine of Kalwaria
on Good Friday 1926,
the dramatic presentation
of the "Via Crucis" takes place.
The father Zapała,
as did his grandfathers,
impersonates the Christ (left).
Karoł Woityła, with his father,
attends the performance.

*Zapała, with the cross,
symbolically ascends Mount Calvary.
A woman, whom tradition
has named Veronica, wipes the face
of Christ and shows
the imprint to the crowd.*

The rite is over and night descends on Kalwaria. The lighting of the fires in the snow signifies the end of the performance.

*To escape from the Germans,
Władek, the son of Zapała,
at his wife's cry of alarm,
jumps from the hay-loft, and rolling
down the slops hides under a bridge
(right).*

The Concentration Camp at Auschwitz
is the scene of the Polish holocaust.
Among the prisoners who each morning
at dawn respond to roll call,
is also the father Zapała.

14 August 1941.
A prisoner is missing at roll call.
The Lager Fuehrer, with a riding whip,
points out the ten men condemned
to die in reprisal.
As one of the condemned men rebels
(lower left), a Catholic priest
asks and is accepted
as a substitute for him.
He is Father Maximilian Kolbe (right).

*Karol Wojtyła, with other students,
in order to escape deportation,
work as day labourers
in the chemical factory of Solvay (right).
But one day, near the entrance to the factory,
Karol is knocked down by a truck.
Wanda, with her brother Marian
and his friend Tadeusz (center,
lower right) goes to the
hospital to visit him.*

The Jewish quarter of Cracow
was destroyed by the Nazis (left).
Helping in the removal
of the debris and the dead bodies
are the men employed in public services.
Marian is among them (right).

*During his work in clearing away
the debris in the Jewish quarter of Cracow,
Tadeusz finds a Jew,
hidden under a panel of wood
in the floor of the house
(right and center).
His name is Jozef Dajches.
The two decide to flee (lower right).*

*Evading the German control,
the two find their first refuge
in the Church of St. Joseph.
Tadek, in the confessional,
asks help of the priest (bottom center),
and after a while the
two leave the presbytery dressed
in religious garb (right)
They join the ranks
of the resistance (lower left).*

*The partisans of Władek receive
Tadek and Jozef on the hills between
Cracow and Kalwaria.
One day they prepare to ambush
a column of German trucks
(lower left).
Another day, while Father Marek
celebrates Mass, they are surprised
by a small enemy reconnaissance plane
(right).*

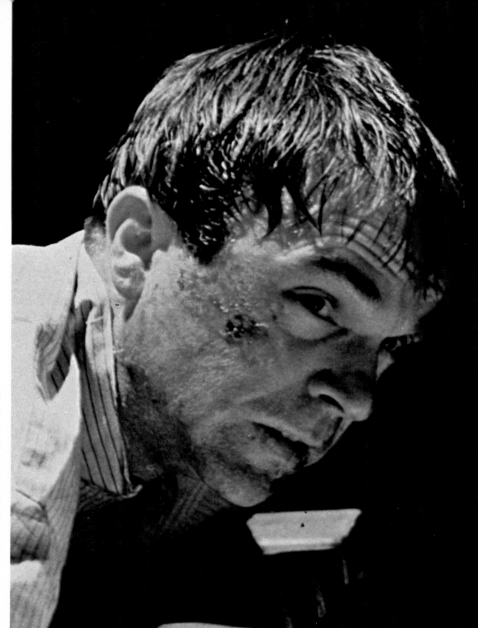

The Nazis place the blame of Tadek's flight on his friend, Marian, who after being tortured, is interned at Auschwitz (left). On August 6, 1944, a search-station is set up by the Germans in Cracow for all able-bodied men. The Archbishop Sapieha (top center) opens a seminary in the city to halt the deportation of his future priests (lower right). Among these young men is Karol Wojtyła.

During the search of "Black Sunday" even Wanda is stopped (top right).

On 17 January 1945 the Red Army
enters Warsaw and two
days later frees Cracow and Lodz.
In the photo are the Russian
armed tanks entering Cracow.
During the work on the film the
Director had to explain to an alarmed
populace over television,
that this was a filming and not
a real invasion.

*After the liberation of Cracow
by the Red Army (right), the people
returned to their homes.
Among the first was Władek,
who after embracing his wife and his
mother, saw once again his
son Staszek, whom he had left
at a tender age (left).*

*After the war the boundaries
of Poland extended towards the West
for 300 kilometers, up to the Oder-Neisse.
A large part of the populace from
the East had to migrate to new territories,
leaving behind them their familiar lands.
Marian, now working in the
Polish repatriation office, travels
on a crowded train (top) where he meets
an old exhausted priest who wishes
to confide in him
his sorrowful secrets (lower panel).*

The feast of the Constitution of 3 May
(which coincides with that of the
Madonna of Jasna Gora) was abolished
by the Government.
A great procession of protest is formed
during which Tadek and Wanda
meet and try to flee together
from the police.

In the Wawel Cathedral, at the altar
of the ancient crypt of St Leonard,
where Polish Kings are buried,
Karol Wojtyła celebrated his First Mass
on All Souls Day, 2 November.
Marian is at his side as acolyte,
and many of his old friends
are present: among them the "Professor",
Wanda and Tadek.

In the new work capital, Nowa Huta,
near Cracow, rise the great iron
works of the Country.
Among the citizens who come here looking
for work is Władek who left his
farm home in Kalwaria.

Arriving at Nowa Huta, Władek presents
himself to the functionary who registers
the personal information of new workers
(left) and asks if he can bring his whole
family to the city.
The new politics wants to penetrate
all sectors of civil life.
The theater also must adapt itself
to the exigencies of socialistic reality.
That is what Jozef Dajches,
having become a functionary of the Party,
asked of the theater company directed
by Mieczysław Kotlarczyk,
called the "Professor" (center
with Wanda). After a fiery discussion,
Wanda left the theater.

Tadek (right), whose civil work found
an outlet in literature,
has written an epic poem on Nowa Huta.
He presented his work at the
new iron-works center during
a public meeting with the workers.
In the assembly he notices Wanda,
who having abandoned the theater,
has found work in the city
in construction (center and left).

The death of his mother recalls Tadek,
after a long absence, to his home,
where he meets the assistant
pastor of S. Floriano, Fr. Wojtyła (left).
Morally and politically in crisis,
he seeks once again the company
of Wanda (right).

In the Fifties came the decision to build
a church in Nowa Huta, which,
at the beginning, was not foreseen.
Marian raises a cross of wood
on the chosen site, but suddenly
the authorities revoke
the permission to build.
It will be Władek Zapała who drives
the bulldozer to break down the cross,
thereby provoking violent
disorder among the people (right).

The friendship between Wanda and Tadek is changed into love. Marian celebrates the nuptials in a church in Cracow (right) because that of Nowa Huta is not yet finished. But work there is going on freely and it will be Cardinal Wojtyła who celebrates one of the first Masses (center right). Jozek, having returned his Party Card, confides to Tadek the reasons for his ideological crisis, following the decline of Stalinism (lower right). Likewise the student Staszek finds it necessary to discuss reforms in socialism in terms of greater respect of civil liberty (top right).

In the spring of '68, Władek Zapała, with the authority of an auxiliary police, prepares to leave his house to check the student protest at the university, in which his son, Staszek, is also participating (left). However, after a confrontation with his son (center) Władek not only renounces his participation in the suppression, but, when the police find anti-State propaganda in his house, he accuses himself instead of Staszek (right).

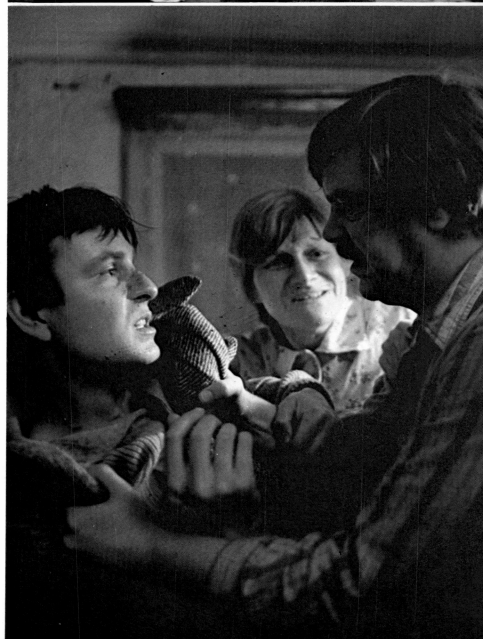

*At the unexpected news of the election
to the Pontificate of Karol Wojtyła,
the people run through the streets
and display a wonderful spirit
of solidarity and joy.
Also Wanda and Tadek join the popular
rejoicing, suppressing their nostalgia
for a friend now unattainable.*

It is June 10, 1979. Pope John Paul II
returned for nine days to his homeland.
In the great public field in Cracow, Błonie,
he sees again among the huge crowd
his old friends: Marian, in a priest's cassock,
Tadek and Wanda,
who receive Holy Communion
from his hands.

(In the following pages)
The last moving greeting to the people
of Poland expresses the Pope's deep
and tender bond with the traditions,
the history, the spiritual patrimony,
but also the hopes ad the struggles
of his homeland.

Film Titles

LORD GRADE
Presents

GIACOMO PEZZALI's

TRANS WORLD FILM - ITC - RAI Production

of

KRZYSZTOF ZANUSSI's
Film
FROM A FAR COUNTRY
Pope John Paul II

Starring
SAM NEILL   CHRISTOPHER CAZENOVE   LISA HARROW

With
MAURICE DENHAM   WARREN CLARKE

Music by
WOJCIECH KILAR

Screenplay by
ANDRZEJ KIJOWSKI and JAN JOZEF SZCZEPANSKI

In collaboration with KRZYSZTOF ZANUSSI

Adapted by DAVID BUTLER. From an idea by DIEGO FABBRI

Artistic Consultant
GASTONE FAVERO

Directed by
KRZYSZTOF ZANUSSI

Produced by
GIACOMO PEZZALI & VINCENZO LABELLA
in Co-operation with FILM POLSKI

CAST

Marian Sam Neill	*Investigating official* Philip Trewinnard
Tadek Christopher Cazenove	*Activist* Simon Dutton
Wanda Lisa Harrow	*Curate* Geoffrey Russell
Władek Warren Clarke	*Official* Matthew Long
Sapieha Maurice Denham	*2nd Security officer* Martin Milman
Józef Jonathan Blake	*1st Security officer* Rupert Frazer
Magda Emma Relph	*German officer* Andrzej Lapicki
Staszek Andrew Seear	*Engineer* Jerzy Stuhr
Władek's wife Carol Gillies	*Wojtyła's father* Andrzej Zarnecki
Władek's mother Anne Dyson	*Young man (Nova Huta)* Tadeusz Bradecki
Curate John Franklyn-Robbins	*Father Kolbe* Kazimierz Kursa
Interrogator James Coyle	*Militiaman* Marek Konrat
Karoł Wojtyła Cezary Morawski	*Captain* Daniel Olbrychski
Worker Timothy Morand	*Nun* Maja Komorowska
Priest John Welsh	*University Professor* Jerzy Nowak
Tadek's mother Kathleen Byron	*Auschwitz prisoner* Tadeusz Hudziak
Professor Zbigniew Zapasiewicz	*Nun* Liliana Glabczynska
Chaplain Philip Latham	*Priest* Edward Lubaszenko
Middle aged woman Georgine Anderson	*Voice of Karoł Wojtyła* Frank Finlay
Chairman David Sibley	*Narrated by* Michael Jayston
Chrystus (Władek's father) Kazimierz Borowiec	

CONTENTS

Printed in Italy by G. Canale & C. S.p.A. - Torino